WHAT SHALL WE

TELL THE

CHILDREN ?

NANCY KOHNER

BBC BOOKS

ACKNOWLEDGEMENTS

I owe particular thanks to Dilys Went,
of Brook Advisory Centres,
for her help in writing this book.
Her knowledge, guidance and support
have been invaluable.

I would also like to thank:

Tony Matthews, Series Producer,
What shall we tell the children?
Kate Cheeseman, Director
Ann Curtis-Clarke, Production Assistant.

Lastly, I would like to thank Tom McGing
for his help and support.

This book is published to accompany the
television series entitled
What Shall we Tell the Children?
which was first broadcast in January 1993
Published by BBC Books,
a division of BBC Enterprises Limited,
Woodlands, 80 Wood Lane
London W12 0TT

First Published 1993
© Nancy Kohner 1993
ISBN 0 563 36762 8
Illustrations by Biz Hull
Set in Palatino by Phoenix Photosetting Ltd, Chatham
Printed and bound in Great Britain by
Clays Ltd, St Ives plc
Cover printed by Clays Ltd, St Ives plc

CONTENTS

INTRODUCTION: WHY TALK ABOUT SEX?

Why is it so hard to talk to children about sex? Is it because we're not sure of the facts? Or we can't find the right words? Or it never seems to be the right moment? Or is it just too embarrassing?

There aren't many subjects that parents don't want their children to learn about, and usually the sooner they learn the better. But sex is somehow different. We say, 'Wait till you're older', 'It'll be better to learn about that at school', 'I'll tell you some other time' . . . and we put off talking about it. Yet many parents look back to their own childhood and, remembering how little they themselves were told about sex, they want to make sure their children know more.

My parents weren't very open, they couldn't talk about sex. I try to be as open as I can with my children because I believe it's better to hear it from your parents than to hear it from other people.

1

My parents never told me anything. My mother never discussed periods, sex or anything with us. My aunt was the person who told me about periods and she terrified me. She told me about how painful they can be. I was really scared. So I was determined my own daughter would know exactly what a period was and why she was having one. I wanted her to know everything.

Wanting your children to learn about sex doesn't make talking about it any easier. For most people, sex is a very private part of their lives and so they find it hard to talk about it in an objective, open way. It's still a taboo subject. Even though the media seems to be full of it, sex is, unfortunately, rarely treated in a serious or sensitive way. Sex in the media is titillating, lurid, romantic, or (very often) a good laugh, but it's hardly ever *real*.

Most of us can make jokes about sex but find it much more difficult to talk about it seriously, especially with our children. It's hard to know how much to say and when to say it. A lot of parents feel it's best to wait until their children start to ask questions – but what if your children don't ask? Or what if they ask someone else, not you? Or perhaps ask too late? In any case, children don't always ask the questions you would expect them to, and sometimes they ask questions that are hard to answer, not because they're embarrassing but because they're complicated. It isn't easy to respond to such deceptively simple questions as 'What are hormones?' or 'How are twins made?' or even 'How do you get HIV?' It's only when children ask these kinds of questions that you may suddenly realize you're not in fact very sure of the answers.

Nor is it easy to deal with the complicated social and moral issues that discussions about sex can raise. Many parents hesitate to tackle subjects like homosexuality, under-age sex, or abortion, although teenagers often debate these issues amongst themselves. It can be hard for parents to accept that their children hold views that are different to their own – views with which parents may disagree.

But whatever the difficulties are that parents experience, children do need to learn about sex. What is more they need to learn about it from an early age, and to *go on* learning about it as they grow up. Children need to learn about it from their parents, as well as from, not instead of, other sources such as school, their friends, or the media.

It's so good being able to talk to your mum and dad, because sometimes you feel silly talking to your friends, and you can't talk to a teacher. I can say anything to my mum and dad.

(13-YEAR-OLD GIRL.)

I think parents should try not to be embarrassed by it, because then it will be easier, for them and for the children. And I think they should say how important sex is, and teach children about the emotions, and say that they can always turn to them and talk to them.

(16-YEAR-OLD GIRL.)

I talk to my mum a lot about sex. If I've got a query I'm not afraid to ask her, because I know that she's going to tell me straight out. She doesn't beat around the bush.

(12-YEAR-OLD GIRL.)

3

Children need to learn about sex for the same reason that they need to know about so much else: it's part of learning about life. But there are other reasons too. Almost from the time they are born, children are aware of sex. They are aware of the people around them and the differences between men and women, and boys and girls. Gradually, as they grow older, their sexual awareness increases. They become more aware of themselves and their bodies, and of each other. They are also bombarded with sexual messages by the media. It would be difficult for a child who watches television, who sees advertisements, who sees newspapers and magazines, to avoid becoming aware of sex, even if only in a vague, unknowing way. So children need to learn about sex in order to make sense of what they see, and to reach a better understanding of themselves, their own sexuality and the sexual world about them.

Children also need to learn about sex so that they can feel more confident in themselves, and be more caring in their relationships with others. Knowing how the human body works can help them feel comfortable with their own bodies and can counter the embarrassment and awkwardness that sometimes comes with puberty. Understanding about sexual behaviour and feelings can help them to understand and accept their own and others' sexuality, and can make it easier for them to manage their own relationships and feelings. Knowing about sex can also help them protect themselves against the risks of unwanted pregnancy, infection or abuse.

A lot of the time you're taught that sex is a bad thing and you shouldn't have it until you're fairly old. But because people are going to have sex, I think they should be taught all the

> *right things about it. Otherwise they just go out and do the*
> *wrong thing, don't use any contraception and get pregnant*
> *and get AIDS.*
> (16-YEAR-OLD GIRL.)

Some parents worry that teaching their children about sex will encourage them to become sexually active at a younger age. But although it seems logical to think that if you know how to do something, you're more likely to do it, in fact children's level of knowledge probably has very little to do with the level of their sexual activity. Research has shown that learning about sex means that children are less vulnerable, and that they are better able to make more informed, responsible decisions about their relationships and sexual behaviour. They may decide to have sex, or they may not. Either way, they can't behave responsibly, either towards themselves or others, unless they're equipped with knowledge.

Children *want* to know about sex. They're curious and interested, just as most adults are, in learning how the human body (*their* body) works, and in finding out how men and women behave and why. They know, too, that they *need* to know about sex – and about more than sex alone.

> *My advice to parents would be just to open up to their*
> *children. Because we need them. We can't always rely on*
> *our school, or the media, or magazines. Our friends some-*
> *times give us completely the wrong view. We need them to*
> *tell us about developing, about growing up, about*
> *changing, and about our feelings. And it wouldn't hurt to*
> *know how they were when they were younger, and how they*
> *felt, and how they grew up.*
> (15-YEAR-OLD GIRL.)

It's a tall order . . . but this book offers some help. It suggests some ways of talking to children about sex and everything to do with sex. It provides factual information, with illustrations to help you explain things clearly. And it looks at some of the sensitive and difficult issues that parents and children have to deal with.

There may be ideas in the book that you don't agree with or feel are not right for you and your family. Discussions between parents and children about sex and relationships are private and personal and each family has its own way of talking. But there may also be some ideas you would like to use, either now or in the future, to help you talk to your children.

TALKING ABOUT SEX

What does it really mean, talking about sex? It means talking about men's and women's bodies, about developing and growing up, about periods and wet dreams, about sexual behaviour, about conception and birth, about contraception and safer sex . . . and much else besides.

It means more than just facts. It means talking about sexuality in all its forms, and about relationships that may or may not be sexual. It means talking about responsibility and risk, about experiences and feelings, and about what it means to respect both oneself and others. It means talking to children about themselves.

In this book, the phrase 'talking about sex' is used to mean all these things.

WHAT CHILDREN SAY

You really need to know from your parents, because your parents have been through all the things that you'll go through. So they're probably the best people to talk to.

If you can't rely on your parents to tell you all you need to know, you get really confused and worried and you just have to rely on your friends.

Parents really worry about having to tell their children about the birds and the bees, because they don't really want their children to grow up. But you've got to tell them, because the children will be so confused if you don't. So you have to tell them. And when you come round to it, it's not so bad.

Parents should give it a go and actually talk to their children and give them a chance, and not just think, 'Oh it's going to be so embarrassing', or 'She's too young', or whatever. Because you're never too young to know what you need to know.

WHAT TO SAY, HOW TO SAY IT

This part of the book is a brief 'how to do it' guide to talking to children about sex. You'll find more suggestions about how to talk about particular topics in The Facts (pages 37 to 138). But there is no one way to talk to children that guarantees success, and what works in one family doesn't work in another. You have to find out what's right for you and your children. What's written here may help you do that.

They shouldn't just tell you the basics. They should tell you everything you want to know when you need to know it. You should be able to talk to your mum and dad about anything.
(13-YEAR-OLD GIRL.)

I can't remember not knowing about sex. It's something my parents have always talked about. I don't think there was a time when they said 'Right, now we're going to tell you about sex'.
(15-YEAR-OLD BOY.)

WHAT DO YOU SAY, AND WHEN?

It's easy to think that children don't know anything about sex until they're told about it. But whether we tell them anything or not, all children know something about sex. They're aware of it even as babies and, as they grow up, they learn about it simply by watching the world about them.

What children lack, until it's given to them, is the information that can help them make sense of what they know. A boy may know he has a penis, but at first he doesn't know it's *called* a penis. He knows that girls and women haven't got a penis, but he doesn't know what they *have* got. He knows that a baby grows inside its mother, but he doesn't know how it got there or, just as puzzling, how it will get out. In other words, children have some bits of the jigsaw but they need to be given the other bits to understand the picture.

There's a lot to understand, and children need to start learning early. The longer we leave talking to them, the more likely they are to make up their own solutions to mysteries like human reproduction. And since no one could really guess the amazing truth, children who aren't given information come up with some very inventive ideas. Adults often find this amusing, or even sweet and innocent, but fiction can get in the way of learning the facts. A child who has reached the age of eight thinking that babies are made when the mother swallows a seed or that babies come from heaven, has to unlearn these beliefs before learning the truth. As a result the child may end up feeling a bit of a fool and perhaps not so confident of new information.

Starting early means that children can learn gradually and build up what they know bit by bit. What they learn at first may be very simple, but so long as it's true, it can lead on to learning more. For example, around the age of five, a child might learn that a baby is made by a mother and a father. By the age of seven, he or she might learn that a baby is made from a man's sperm and a woman's ovum. Around the age of nine, there may be some understanding of sexual intercourse and how the sperm and ovum meet. And so on.

Some children ask questions about sex, but many don't, and not asking isn't necessarily a sign that a child isn't interested, or puzzled, or worried. Some children are too shy, or just don't put their questions into words. Or, not knowing enough, they simply don't know what to ask. No one can ask a question about something they don't know anything about. So instead of waiting for questions, parents have to make the first move and try to give their children the information they need *at the time they need it*.

◆ By the time they start school if not before, children need to know the correct words for the main sexual organs, both male and female. They need these words so that they can think, talk and ask questions about sex without difficulty or embarrassment. They also need words so they can learn about the differences between the sexes. Understanding the real differences between men and women and boys and girls is vital for young children. They can't learn anything else about sex until they've gained this understanding.

11

◆ Children need to build up an understanding about how babies are conceived, develop and are born. This understanding comes gradually and children can begin to learn before starting school. At first what you say may be extremely simple, but it can still be honest.

◆ From as early as possible, children need to learn about the risk of abuse. They need to learn skills to protect themselves: how to recognize danger, what to do (and what not to do), who to trust and who can help. For more about this, see page 157.

◆ Well before they reach puberty, by about the age of eight or nine, children need to have learnt in outline about the changes that puberty brings and how they can be helped to cope with, for example, periods, erections and wet dreams. No child should have to experience these changes without understanding what is happening and why. It's also important that boys understand changes in girls, and vice versa.

◆ Around the age of 11 or 12, well before the time when they might choose to become sexually active, children need to understand not only about intercourse itself and other sexual behaviour but also about contraception and safer sex. They need to have practical, detailed knowledge about how they can protect themselves from infection and unwanted pregnancy.

    To some parents, this may seem early to learn

about sexual behaviour. But recent surveys have

shown that the pressures on children can be
extreme. For example, it's estimated that in
England as many as 30 per cent of girls under 16
have had experience of sexual intercourse. Many
more will have had experience of relationships
that are more or less sexual, even though they
have not had intercourse.

♦ From the beginning, children need to learn about
human experiences, not just physical processes.
Whether you're talking to your children about
periods, or intercourse, or having a baby, they
need to know how it feels emotionally as well as
what happens physically.

*It's not right, just to say this is this and that is that. You
want to know how you'll feel, and all the emotions you'll
go through.*
(12-YEAR-OLD GIRL.)

HOW DO YOU SAY IT?

*She doesn't talk as if she's my mother. She makes it like
she's my friend, and she really helps me when I don't
understand things and I need help or I've got problems.*
(12-YEAR-OLD GIRL.)

*My mum explains things in a way that I feel comfortable
with and she feels comfortable. I think that's important. I
don't think the parent should just explain it straight out
and not listen to the child's views.*
(12-YEAR-OLD GIRL.)

13

Very few people feel completely relaxed talking about sex. But children, whether they're toddlers or teenagers, learn a lot more, and learn a lot more easily, if you can talk with them in an open, relaxed kind of way.

◆ Rather than sitting down specially to talk about sex, try to let the subject crop up naturally and, when it does, talk about it. (Sometimes, of course, you have to *make* it crop up naturally. See Making Opportunities, page 25.) Be as easy and natural as you can. If you find this difficult, see Sparing Blushes – Getting Over Embarrassment, page 21.

◆ Try to be open about sex, but make it private too. It's important to treat sex as ordinary and to be matter-of-fact, but you also have to acknowledge that sex can't be talked about anywhere or at any time. It isn't just that other people (in the super-market queue, for example) might be embarrassed or disapproving, but also that children need to learn that sex is a private not a public matter.

◆ Talk a little every now and then and go over the same ground more than once. Subjects like menstruation and conception are complicated and it takes children time to understand them. It helps if they can learn a little, go away and think about it, come back and talk a bit more, maybe ask some questions, and so on. It's also a good idea to check they have really understood what you've said.

I told my daughter about periods and I thought I'd done a really good job explaining about it in a fairly simple way.

14

*It wasn't until later I realized she thought that once you
started periods, you bled all the time for the rest of your
life.*

◆ Make sure you yourself know at least the basic
   facts. There's nothing like having to explain
   something to someone else to test your
   knowledge. If you feel at all unsure, check your
   facts before you start (see pages 37 to 138).

   On the other hand, don't feel you have to know
   everything. Who could? Children have a knack of
   asking difficult and unexpected questions and you
   may find you don't know the answers. So be
   prepared to find out more, maybe with your child,
   when you need to. See the list of helpful books on
   pages 165 to 167.

◆ Be low-key and don't overdo it. Sometimes
   parents are so well intentioned, and so keen for
   their children to be well informed, they talk about
   sex a bit too much. Some children listen patiently
   but switch off. Others greet the umpteenth
   conversation about periods with 'Oh no, not sex
   again!' You may need to find other ways of giving
   information – using books, for example. See
   Making Opportunities, page 25.

◆ Try to answer questions at the time they're
   asked. Children are usually much more ready to
   listen if you can do this. Sometimes, of course,
   it's not possible. If your five-year-old asks in a
   loud voice in front of the condoms in the
   chemist's, 'What are those for?', you'll probably

have to say, 'I'll explain later'. But then keep your promise – on the way home, perhaps.

◆ Do your utmost to help your children feel they can talk to you, or ask you, about *anything*. Children pick up information and ideas about sex from lots of different sources – from school, their friends, television, films, books, adverts, adult jokes, newspapers . . . . They need someone to help them sort out all this information. They also need to know there's someone they can turn to with any problem or dilemma – someone who won't laugh at their fears or anxieties and will try to understand. That's true for younger children as well as for teenagers.

◆ Try to adapt what you say so that it's right for your child's age and understanding. This isn't as easy as it sounds. Some aspects of sex are very hard to explain in simple terms and adults can easily miss out pieces of information that seem obvious to them but are far from obvious to small children.

My daughter asked me from the back of the car one day how babies are made. When I'd finished explaining it to her, she thought about it for a long time and after a bit I asked if there was anything she didn't understand. She said, 'Do you take your knickers off first?'

If you can, have a two-way conversation. It makes it easier to know whether your child understands what you're saying.

Looking at pictures together will also help you explain things clearly. You could use the pictures in The Facts (pages 37 to 138), or look at the books for children listed on pages 165 to 167. Or draw your own pictures or diagrams. You don't have to be a great artist, although you do have to know enough to get the right bits in roughly the right places.

◆ Try to show your children the same respect as you would want them to show you and other people. Talking to a child about starting periods, or having wet dreams, or to a teenager about sexual behaviour, is talking about something very personal. It's important to be straightforward, but you need to be sensitive as well.

When you're talking about sex, you don't have to talk about your own sex life. In fact, children need to learn that your sex life is private. But children deserve privacy too. As they grow older, you have to accept that you won't and can't know everything about *their* sexual behaviour. For more about this, see pages 150 to 152.

◆ Try to talk about feelings as well as facts. The facts about sex don't make much sense unless you can put them in the context of real human relationships and emotions.

FINDING A LANGUAGE

Words are important. Children can't begin to understand about sex if they haven't got words to think with.

Families often have their own words for parts of the body (especially the sexual parts) and for functions like urinating and defecating, and they often feel more comfortable with their own words than they do with the correct terms. Lots of people still hesitate to use words like 'penis' and 'vagina'. But these are the words that everyone can understand. Family words are okay in the family, but when you need to talk to someone else (like a doctor), you need a language that's generally understood.

It helps children enormously to know the correct words for the parts and functions of the body. It gives them confidence, takes away mystery, and gives them a language for thinking and talking. If they learn these words from the start (maybe alongside family words), they'll feel comfortable about using them and can also learn, as they do about other words, not to use these words out of context. Parents who feel self-conscious can get in a bit of practice at using words like 'labia', 'vulva', 'penis', 'testes' etc. while they're changing a nappy or giving a bath. Instead of 'Let's clean your bottom', you simply say, 'Let's clean your vulva' – and after a while, it sounds just as natural.

Children need words for the sexual parts of their own body *and* words for the sexual parts of the opposite sex. Without this vocabulary, they can't begin to understand the differences between the sexes, and this understanding is needed as early as possible. They also need words for what they can see, and equally for what's invisible. See page 43 for a list of words that it's useful for children to know.

Some words that you might use aren't exactly incorrect but they can be misleading. If you talk, for example, about a baby growing inside its mother's 'tummy', children can think that this is literally true. Quite a lot of children who haven't been given any facts about reproduction and who have to make up their own explanations, decide that the baby must grow in its mother's stomach and be fed by the food she eats. Using the word 'tummy' or 'stomach' supports the idea. 'Bottom' is another misleading word. Some people use it to mean a girl's sexual organs (vulva) as well as the area around her anus and her bottom (or buttocks) into the bargain. 'Seed', instead of ovum, can make a child think of seeds that are sown in the garden, and an 'egg' is more likely to be thought of as the breakfast variety that comes in a shell. Although all these words seem easier to understand because they are known and familiar, they can really make understanding more difficult.

Older children pick up other words, mostly four letters long, that they will want to use or want explained. Some parents feel more at home with these words themselves. You may find it easier, for example, to explain about 'wanking' than 'masturbating', to talk about 'coming' rather than 'having an orgasm' or 'ejaculating', 'come' rather than 'semen'. Others don't use or like these words but want their children to know them so that they will know what's meant if they hear the words, can't be shocked (and won't shock others by using them), and won't be laughed at by their friends for being ignorant or (what's maybe worse) posh. It's probably helpful if children know both the correct words and the slang, and you can then decide between you what words are acceptable to use.

> *We were out in the garden having a game of cricket and he caught me with a stump. So we were talking about why that hurt so much. I explained they were testicles, but I said, 'You probably call them balls, or nuts, at school.' Because if he went back to school and talked about his testicles, he'd be laughed at.*

The language you use isn't only important for accuracy. Words say more than they mean. You might use 'making love' to mean the same as 'having sex', but the words say very different things about the same act. Children need to learn more than the facts about sex: hearing about the feelings and experiences is just as

---

SEX BY ANY OTHER NAME . . .

These are some of the non-sexual words that you might use when talking with children about sex. They all say something about what sex can mean.

affection	love
caress	loving
caring	please
close	pleasure
commitment	relaxed
considerate	respect
excitement	sensitive
gentle	stroke
hold	touch
hug	trust
kiss	warm

---

some children (though not all) become more self-conscious and want more privacy.

> *My son's 12 and he's never been inhibited at all but suddenly now he won't even let me in the bathroom when he's having a bath. He's still quite happy to come and sit at the end of the bath if I'm in the bath or getting dressed. He's not embarrassed or uncomfortable about that. But he's started closing doors now. I feel it's shutting me out a little bit, but I realize he needs it – a bit of his own space. He's not inhibited in any other way. He still kisses me and is very affectionate and close.*

Boys seem more likely to feel embarrassed than girls, and they also seem to be more silent on the subject of sex, which can make talking difficult:

> *My daughter was very easy to talk to because from being very young she talked and asked questions, so it was just a natural part of her development. My son was much more difficult because he would never ask questions. But he was always there listening. So you'd have to create situations where, say, I could get my daughter talking or looking at a book, really for the benefit of my son. And he would just be sitting nearby listening. But he would never come and talk to me, and I don't think he really talked to his dad either.*

There are ways you can get over embarrassment – yours or your children's.

◆ Try to talk when you're doing something. It helps not to have to look each other in the eye, and to

23

have something to do with your hands. Chat while you're peeling potatoes or washing up, or when you're driving somewhere in the car. Look at a book together (see the list of books on pages 165 to 167). Use pencil and paper and illustrate what you're trying to explain. If you're not very good at drawing, this should give you something to laugh about together.

♦ Laughing together can help a lot – proper laughter, not embarrassed giggles. Sex does have its funny side and laughter is one of the best ways of relieving stress, although you've got to be sure that you're not making jokes just to get out of saying anything honest or direct.

As children get older, laughing together about sex can be a way of keeping the subject out in the open.

I had some friends round. We were talking about two teachers at our school who'd just got married. The man was very tall and the woman very short. My mum said 'Oh well, everyone's the same size in bed', and everyone laughed. Afterwards my friends said, wasn't I lucky to have a mum who'd joke like that.
(13-YEAR-OLD BOY.)

♦ Be honest and admit you feel embarrassed. If you can admit to finding talking difficult but do it anyway, then maybe your children will be able to do the same.

My mum's very embarrassed about sex. When she was a child it was never talked about. But she always talks to me about it. She's still embarrassed, but she talks to me. And I think that's fantastic. She's brilliant.
(12-YEAR-OLD GIRL.)

◆ Children may feel embarrassed talking to one of their parents, but fine talking to the other.

I feel it's easier for me to talk to my mum. I feel I can't talk to my dad. I don't know why but I just get embarrassed and I know my dad would get embarrassed. But with my mum, I feel I can really talk to her.
(12-YEAR-OLD GIRL.)

Or children find it embarrassing to talk to their parents, but okay to talk to other people. Sometimes it can help to hand over to someone else, provided you know you can trust them (see Does It Have To Be You? on page 28).

MAKING OPPORTUNITIES

If you've got a child who asks questions very readily and talks a lot with you about anything and everything, then talking about sex won't be much of a problem. In fact, you may have to be clear that there are times and places that are not all right for discussions about sex. But not all children are talkative and sometimes you have to bring the subject up yourself. Try to do this as naturally as you can.

25

◆ Use a book. There are a lot of books written for children and teenagers (see pages 165 to 167 for a selection). With small children, you can look at books together and talk as you go. With older children, try saying something like, 'I thought you'd like to have a look at this. I thought it was quite good. See what you think.'

◆ Watch a television programme or a video together and talk about it afterwards. It doesn't have to be a sex education programme. Lots of television programmes and films give you the chance to talk about sex and sexual issues, and often in a way that children find more realistic and easier to understand.

We had a very funny scene in our house not too long ago. There was a film being advertised on the television, and there was a woman screaming at her husband, 'I faked all those orgasms!' So of course my daughter said, 'What's an orgasm?' And I just froze . . . I said, 'Well, go upstairs and look at that book you've got'. And then she shouted down the stairs, 'I don't understand this, Mum.' So I explained then of course. It was a really good way of it happening, because I was able then to talk about masturbating and it brought that out into the open. So I was quite pleased, in fact.

◆ Television commercials, and adverts or articles in magazines and newspapers can sometimes help you talk, especially now that contraceptives and sanitary towels are more widely and explicitly advertised.

◆ If you want to talk about 'growing up' and puberty, family photos can help. Look at pictures of your children as babies; or even photos of yourself when you were growing up.

────

◆ Bathtime is usually a good time to talk, whether it's your child or you or both of you who are in the bath.

When I was pregnant, my daughter and I went on having baths together. They were really lovely warm, relaxed times when we could talk about anything. She asked me a lot about the baby, and about her body and mine, and it was the easiest thing in the world to talk about it.

Bedtime, when you're saying goodnight and the light's turned down, is another time when you can often talk easily about intimate things.

────

◆ Babies can be useful for prompting conversations, especially when you're changing a nappy.

────

◆ If you're happy to change a tampon or a sanitary towel while your child is in the bathroom with you (and when they're small, it's sometimes hard to avoid it), that can make explaining about periods very easy. Some women find this impossible and if you can't or don't want to do it, don't feel you have to.

Children often like to watch their fathers shaving. It makes good entertainment, and it's a chance to talk about the whole business of growing up.

> *I didn't have any problems. I was happy to undress when she was about, so it was easy to explain what pubic hair was, or that one day she would have breasts. She used to dress up in my shoes and clothes, and put on my bras, so I could explain that one day she'd wear a bra as well.*

◆ Try to link up with what's being done at school. The school may let you know when they will be teaching about sex and what they will be doing. You can back this up at home by asking and talking about it. (For more about sex education in school, see pages 32 to 34).

DOES IT HAVE TO BE YOU?

Some parents feel very anxious about teaching their children about sex, partly because they feel embarrassed and partly because they feel they won't do it well enough. They would rather children got their sex education at school.

> *I believe that schools should teach it, because parents do find it difficult to talk about and they get embarrassed. And I think if the school could take some of that away, it would be a great help. Then we would know that our children were given correct information and told exactly what's what. It would be like history, or geography – just a part of their school education.*

But while schools can give children clear information, illustrated with visual aids, and the benefit of talking things over in a group, parents can give something to their children that school sex education cannot, no matter how well it's done.

Lots of parents think that the school should tell you about sex, so they leave it to the school. But I think that parents should tell you, because you need to have someone close to you that you can talk to about sex.
(16-YEAR-OLD GIRL.)

Parents know their children in a way teachers never can, know what they worry about, know what they need to know. Parents can put information about sex in a family context and, if they wish, in a religious context too. Parents can make information personal, warm, loving – and very much more relevant.

So does that mean it has to be you who talks about every aspect of sex with your child? Certainly it is better for you to talk to your child than to leave him or her to find out from books, or from friends. Friends are a notorious source of inaccurate information, and wrong information is sometimes very damaging.

I'd heard from a friend that when you started your periods, there was this enormous gush of blood and the whole of the back of your skirt was stained. So for weeks I went around glancing behind, just to make sure this wasn't happening to me. And when I did actually start, I didn't recognize it because it wasn't anything like this gush of blood.

Books, too, may give only half the story:

29

The book I had gave a fairly clinical description of the sex organs and what they looked like, and what they looked like when they were cut up, which was completely unreal. And something about the sex act itself. That was about it. But the trouble with the book was that I didn't have any context to put it in. There was no description of how it might be for me as a person. So it was a bit irrelevant really.

But important though parents are, you may feel that you can't supply all the facts your child needs, or that there are subjects you just can't talk about. Sometimes this is to do with your own upbringing and the way you now feel about that as an adult and a parent.

Sex has become much more openly talked about and I think we have to recognize that. I'm a Sikh and I come from quite a traditional Sikh family. I was brought up to believe that sex is something you take part in after marriage. But you can't expect your children to take on board the values you have without also taking on board the influences of the Western society they've grown up and been schooled in. So I think we have to talk about it more. But it's very difficult if you haven't had that background to actually open yourself up to your children.

One-parent families may also have particular concerns. It's obviously impossible to talk about how a man feels if you're a woman, and vice versa. This can be a difficulty in two-parent families too, if one parent doesn't want to talk about sex.

> *I know he needs to talk about these things with a man,*
> *and I can't fulfil that role for him. There's lots of things I*
> *can do as a mother, taking on the traditional father roles.*
> *I do woodwork with him, I climb trees with him, I ride*
> *bikes with him. If he wants to go fishing, I might even try*
> *and do that with him. But I can't empathize with him*
> *about what it's like for him to be growing up and the*
> *feelings and the emotions that he has as his body changes*
> *and develops. I can't do that, and I have to try and find,*
> *or he has to try and find, a man with whom he can talk*
> *about those things.*

Parents who are homosexual may also have to think carefully about how they want their children to learn about sex. It's no easier, of course, for a heterosexual parent to talk about homosexuality than for a homosexual parent to talk about heterosexuality, but being in a minority brings particular pressures, both for parents and children. Children are aware of this and need to be able to think and talk about it.

Children themselves sometimes like to talk to other people as well as their parents. Although family closeness can help, sometimes it can add to embarrassment and it can be easier for children to talk about some things to people who they feel are less emotionally involved. In any case, it can be good to hear different views and get a different perspective, or to have the facts reinforced by having them explained in a slightly different way.

You may want to think about encouraging your child to talk to other people – grandparents, other adults, or older brothers, sisters or friends whom you can trust and whom your child feels comfortable with.   **31**

You can set this up, or just suggest it to your child. It's probably wise to check with the other person first, to be sure they don't mind and so they can be prepared.

SEX EDUCATION IN SCHOOL

It's helpful to know what sex education your child's school provides, and how and when it's given. Then you can pick up at home on some of the topics that are taught or discussed in the classroom. You may in any case feel that you'd like to know what the school does in this subject area.

Both primary and secondary schools must by law have a sex education policy, and it is the school governors' responsibility to devise that policy. The governors work with the staff to decide the content of sex education in the school and how it is taught.

You as a parent can ask to see your school's sex education policy. You might want to do this through your PTA (parent-teacher association) if you've got one, or by talking with the head teacher or a member of staff, perhaps with a group of other parents. You can hear about the thinking behind the policy and how it is put into practice, and talk about how you can best support the teachers and reinforce what's taught at school by talking at home.

What's included in sex education, and the way it is taught, varies widely from school to school. But sex education is included in the science national curriculum, so it is compulsory for all schools to cover certain areas. For example, according to the national curriculum, children aged 11 to 14 must learn about the human life cycle, changes during adolescence, and the effects of bacteria and viruses, including HIV.

The National Curriculum Council produces guidance for schools on what should be covered at different stages between the ages of five and 16. This guidance links sex education with other health education topics such as family life education, and shows how sex education can include a range of ideas and information. For example, between the ages of five and seven, children's sex education might include:

- learning the names of parts of the body.
- understanding what 'male' and 'female' mean.
- learning about personal safety (for example, that individuals have rights over their own bodies).
- understanding about how people learn to live and work together.

You should be able to look at a copy of the National Curriculum Council's *Curriculum Guidance No. 5* at your local library, or at your child's school. For details, see page 167. Another publication produced for teachers but useful for parents who are interested in their child's sex education at school is *A Framework for School Sex Education*, produced by the Sex Education Forum (details on page 167). This is a document which has been endorsed by 21 organizations concerned with young people, and which defines essential knowledge, skills and attitudes to be taught in schools.

Very occasionally, parents don't want their children to take part in certain sessions in a school sex education course, perhaps because they hold strong religious views. If, for whatever reason, a parent doesn't want his or her child to be taught about sex at school, then he or she can apply to the school governors and ask for their child to be withdrawn from that particular session. But it's worth giving this careful thought. Children who are taken out of lessons can sometimes be singled out and teased. Or they may simply get an inaccurate version of the lesson they've missed from their friends. So, before asking for your child to be taken out of a class, it's usually best to try to talk over objections or difficulties with the school.

Keeping in touch with the school, and knowing what's happening in sex education, will mean that you can back up what your child is told at school by talking things over at home. Teachers are usually pleased to have this kind of support and welcome contact with parents.

BEING POSITIVE

He asked me when he was about eight or nine years old, 'Is it nice when a man puts his penis inside you?' and I said 'Yes, it can be the nicest thing in the world, as long as you've got the right partner, somebody you care for, and you love each other. . . . Then it's the most wonderful thing.'

Considering that most people do feel positive about sex (though possibly less so about such necessities as menstruation and contraception), it's surprising how easy it is to be negative when you're talking about it. Because you're anxious, and concerned for your child's safety and well-being, you can easily find yourself giving a

34

lecture when you'd meant to have a chat. There can be a lot of 'don'ts' and very few 'do's'.

But children need to understand that sex is, or should be, loving, and that it can, or should, give pleasure. Giving children information about sex should help them to feel positive about it, not frightened or put off.

When I was a teenager, I was frightened of sex. I was told so many stories about how it hurts and I was terrified. But none of my children are frightened of sex. I think my oldest girl is actually looking forward to her first experience. I'm happy about that because I know she also knows how to take care of herself and I know she expects a lot of a relationship and wouldn't sleep around.

Talking about sex as reproduction can be hard, but for most parents, talking about sex as pleasure is a lot harder. They fear the questions they might be asked, such as 'Do you like doing it?' or 'What does it feel like?' If you're asked questions like these, you don't have to answer from a personal point of view but you can explain that most people enjoy sex, maybe not the first few times they do it but later on. You can say that it's almost impossible to describe what it feels like but that it's exciting, and relaxing, and makes your body feel extraordinarily good. You can, if you wish, say that sex is *more* enjoyable if it takes place within a caring relationship because it becomes an expression of how two people feel about each other.

Children also need to value and feel positive about their own bodies, and respect other people's. So the way they learn about their bodies, from babyhood onwards, is very important. A three-year-old who is

35

told that holding his penis is 'dirty', or a nine-year-old who is told about 'the curse', learns something very negative about sex and about themselves. Although it's probably unrealistic to think that girls could look forward to starting periods, growing up should be a positive experience for all children, and even menstruation, as part of that, can be welcomed.

> *She'd been away on a school trip and on the last day she woke up to find her period had started. And when I met her from the coach, she greeted me by saying, 'Mum, something's happened', and I said, 'What?' and she said 'I've started my period!' And she was so excited and everybody had to know. Her father congratulated her and I was just so pleased that she was so relaxed about it, no hang-ups, wasn't embarrassed, wanted to tell all her friends. . .*

Being positive about sex doesn't mean romanticizing it. The 'don'ts' of sex education are very important, especially for a generation of children facing the risk of AIDS. More and more children are now sexually active under the legal age of 16, and their futures depend on their knowledge of risk and how to minimize it. But just as they shouldn't have to discover risk by accident, they shouldn't have to discover pleasure by accident either. They have a right to enjoy sex, as well as a responsibility to care for themselves and for others.

THE
FACTS

No one can talk clearly about a subject if they're not sure of the facts. And faced by their children's questions, many parents find they're not quite so sure of the facts as they thought they were. So this part of the book sets out the information that, sooner or later, you'll need to give your children, or check that they know. The six main sections are.

- **Bodies** (p 39)
- **Puberty** (p 58)
- **Sex** (p 77)
Babies:
Conception, pregnancy and birth (p 91)
Contraception and Family Planning (p 110)
Sexually Transmitted Diseases – STDs (p 125)

In each of these sections there's guidance on talking about the subject, suggestions about what children need to know, and illustrated factual information.

Some of the factual information in this part of the book may seem very obvious. But even the most obvious facts can be hard to communicate. For example, explaining sexual intercourse to a child isn't difficult from a factual point of view, but it *is* very difficult to find words that are acceptable and appropriate. The words and pictures used in this section will help you to talk comfortably with your children about sex.

There are some facts that some parents may choose not to give their children. You need to make your own decisions about this. But even if you decide not to open up a subject yourself, you'll still need to be able to respond to your children's questions (often quite unexpected and difficult ones) and the information given on the following pages will help you do that.

Not all children need the same information at the same age so there are no rules to follow about what information should be given when. But this part of the book includes some suggestions about timing, and there's more about this on pages 10 to 13.

You may want to look at some of the illustrations and diagrams with your children. It's often easier to explain something with a picture to help you, and it's certainly easier to understand a complicated process like conception if you can look at a picture as well as listen and talk about it. Most of the books for children listed on pages 165 to 167 also include pictures.

BODIES

TALKING ABOUT BODIES

◆   Children can't begin to understand how the
    human body works unless they have some
    understanding of basic anatomy. From very early
    on, they're naturally curious about their own and
    other people's bodies, and they want and need
    information.

    At first, they'll be interested in the parts they
    can see and it's important to put names to the
    parts and to explain what each part is for. Then
    they need to know and understand about the
    internal organs. Talking about what's outside and
    visible can lead to talking about what's inside and
    invisible. For example, explaining about the anus
    can lead to explaining about the back passage and
    about how faeces are excreted.

◆   It helps if you can talk about the sexual parts of
    the body in much the same way as you talk about
    the other parts. In fact, it sometimes helps to talk
    about the sexual parts *at the same time as* other
    parts, looking at pictures together. For example:
    'Here's the stomach, where your food is digested.
    Here are your lungs, which you use for breathing.
    Here's your womb, where a baby could grow if
    you want to become a mother later on . . .' and so
    on. If the sexual parts of the body are only talked
    about at certain times and in certain ways,
    children quickly come to feel that these parts of

39

the body are different and embarrassing. That makes it hard for them to ask direct questions and learn from the answers they're given.

◆ Some parents are happy to dress and undress in front of their children, bath, go to the toilet, change a sanitary towel . . . and so on. Others find this hard, and some feel that it is wrong and undesirable. It's obviously not worth trying to do anything you feel uncomfortable about or, as children get older, anything *they* feel uncomfortable about. Even so, it may be that young children who are used to seeing their parents naked will be less embarrassed about their own bodies and will find it easier to ask questions and learn. Small children who have brothers or sisters can also learn about and get used to bodies if they dress or bath together; and they might do the same with friends.

◆ When you're talking to children about the human body, it's important to be aware that you're giving them information *about themselves*. What you say is quite likely to influence the way they feel, not just about their bodies but also about themselves as people. If you can manage to talk without embarrassment, and to be accepting and positive about every part and function of the human body, it will help them to feel the same.

◆ The Book List on pages 165–167 includes publications for children about the human body.

BODIES: WHAT CHILDREN NEED TO KNOW

============== LEARNING A LANGUAGE ==============

Although families often have their own private words for the sexual parts of the body, children also need to learn the proper words and be able to use them. This is especially important once a child starts school and begins to spend more time with other children and adults. It can be difficult for a teacher or any other adult to understand or help a child who can only use 'family' words.

Knowing words that everyone will understand can also help children to cope if, for example, they are taken to the doctor or have to go into hospital. These situations can be stressful enough for children without the added complications of not being able to make themselves understood or understand what's said to them.

Learning the words for the sexual parts of the body is also important so that children can think about and ask questions. The proper words make sex a proper, acceptable subject to be interested in, and make it possible to talk about it in a more objective way. A child who only knows family (and maybe quite funny) words is more than likely to feel that sex is something that shouldn't be spoken about, or that it's something to giggle over, or they may be afraid of being laughed at.

The basic words that children need to know are listed on page 43. Out of all these words the one that people seem least likely to teach their children is clitoris. Maybe this is because it's the only organ (in men or women) which exists just for pleasure. So if children ask, 'What's the clitoris for?' you have to feel able to

41

explain that rubbing it gently, or having it rubbed, gives a good feeling. Or maybe parents don't teach their children about the clitoris because it's hidden and easy to ignore. But as it's a very important organ for women, it's best to acknowledge its existence right from the start and give it a place in children's vocabulary. How can girls or boys begin to understand about women's sexual feelings otherwise?

SEX DIFFERENCES

Many adults overestimate children's understanding of sex differences. It may seem very obvious that a man has a penis and a scrotum and so is different from a woman who has a clitoris, vagina and womb, but this isn't always so obvious to small children. Many children go on asking very basic questions about sex differences for some years, and maybe for longer than you would expect. You need to be able to deal with questions like the ones below. You'll need to think about the answers you want to give – the answers given here are just suggestions.

Q *Why don't girls have a penis?*
A Because they have a vulva, vagina and womb instead. That's what makes them a girl.
   And/or:
A They don't need one because they pee (urinate) through a small hole in the vulva. A girl has a clitoris. The clitoris is a bit like a penis but very small and you can't see it. The clitoris isn't used for peeing, but it feels good when it's touched.

LEARNING THE WORDS

It helps children to know the correct words for the sexual parts of the body. These are words that they might have learnt (or might be learning) around the age of five:

anus	testes (or testicles)
breasts	vulva
nipples	clitoris
penis	vagina

These are words that could be added when your child is between about five and eight years old:

navel	ovaries
bladder	ovum
urine	male
opening of the	scrotum
urethra (or 'hole	sperm
for urine')	sexual intercourse
female	(or 'making love')
womb (or uterus)	fertilization

All these words are explained on pages 46 to 57.

Q *Why do men have more hair on their bodies than women?*

A It's one of the differences between men and women. There are different chemicals inside a man's body and these chemicals make hair grow. But not all men are hairy – some have much more hair on their bodies than others. Some women have quite a lot of body hair too.

Q *Why do women have breasts?*

A When a woman has a baby, her breasts fill with milk and the baby sucks on the nipple to drink the milk. That's how a mother feeds her baby.

Q *Why do boys pee standing up, and girls pee sitting down?*

A Boys pee out of a small hole at the end of their penis, so the pee comes out at the front. Girls pee out of a small hole in their vulva, so the pee comes out underneath.

UNDERSTANDING DEVELOPMENT

Children are also interested in the differences between their own and adults' bodies. They notice the ways in which bodies grow and change, and the differences between individuals. In places like the changing rooms at the swimming-pool they may well want to tell everyone exactly what's so interesting about people's varying sizes and shapes.

The pictures on pages 66 to 69 show how the male and female bodies change from babyhood to adulthood. Children often like to work out which person in the picture is most like them, or most like others in the family, and looking at the pictures together can give a good starting point for parents and children to begin talking about development.

These are the sort of questions you might be asked. The answers you give will depend on how old your child is and how much he or she understands already, but these are some ideas.

Q *Why do men and women have hair on their bodies but children don't?*

A Growing more hair on your body is part of growing up. When you're about 11 or 12, you begin to grow more body hair and your body starts to change in other ways too until it's more like an adult's body.

Q *When will I grow breasts?*

A They'll probably start to grow when you're about ten. Maybe a bit later. They'll be small at first then get bigger.

Q *When is a girl old enough to have a baby?*

A A girl *could* have a baby as soon as she starts to ovulate – that is, as soon as her ovaries start to produce ova, or egg cells. That's when she's around ten years old – maybe a bit earlier, maybe later. It happens at about the same time as her periods start. But a girl can't make a baby on her own. A man and a woman make a baby together and to do that you need to be much older. Even then, you may choose not to have a baby.

For more about development, see Puberty, pages 58 to 76.

BODIES: THE FACTS

☐══════════☐ THE FEMALE SEX ORGANS ☐══════════☐

Girls and women can see their external sex organs if they use a hand mirror and hold their labia apart, as in the illustration. By holding back the outer lips, it's possible to see the inner lips, the clitoris and the vaginal opening. Not everyone feels comfortable about looking at themselves or handling themselves in this way, but it is difficult to understand your body if you don't look at it properly.

The VULVA is another word for the female genitals – that is, the sex organs that are outside the body.

The LABIA (or LIPS) are folds of skin which close over the vulva. There are the LABIA MAJORA (the OUTER LIPS) and the LABIA MINORA (the INNER LIPS). Labia vary a lot in size and shape. In some women, the inner lips are larger and show outside the outer lips.

The CLITORIS is a little smooth bump at the front and top of the vulva. In a grown woman it is about the size of a cherry stone. It has a little hood of skin which partly covers it. The clitoris is very sensitive. When a woman touches her clitoris in the right sort of gentle way, or when her partner touches it for her, it can give her a very good feeling. Like a man's penis, a woman's clitoris becomes swollen and erect when a girl or woman is sexually excited.

There are two openings in the vulva. The opening of the URETHRA (the tube that leads down from the bladder) is small and difficult to see. This is where urine comes out. The VAGINAL OPENING is larger and quite easy to see, roughly in the middle of the vulva. There is also a third opening, further back, outside the vulva.

46

This is the ANUS, the opening for the RECTUM, or back passage. The area between the vaginal opening and the anus is called the PERINEUM.

In some girls, the vaginal opening is partly covered by a very thin skin called the HYMEN. An intact (unbroken) hymen used to be thought of as a sign of virginity – that is, a sign that a woman had not had sexual intercourse – because the first time a girl or a woman has intercourse, the hymen may (but doesn't always) get stretched and torn, and it may bleed. But very often the hymen is torn in other ways – for example, by playing sport, doing gymnastics, dancing, or by using tampons. No one (not even a doctor) can always tell whether or not someone has had sexual intercourse by looking at the hymen.

Girls and women can see their external organs (their vulva) by holding the labia gently apart and looking in a mirror.

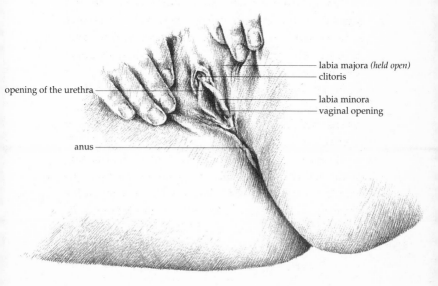

opening of the urethra

labia majora *(held open)*
clitoris

labia minora
vaginal opening

anus

The VAGINA is a muscular tube leading from the vulva to the womb. It's about 10 cm (4 in) long in a grown woman. It doesn't go straight up inside the body but tilts backwards at an angle, pointing towards the small of the back. It is very soft and stretchy, so it can stretch round a man's erect penis during sexual inter-

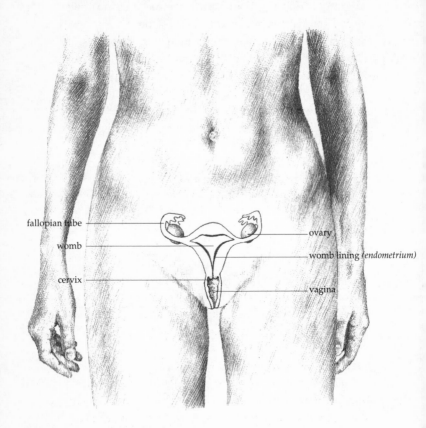

fallopian tube

ovary

womb

womb lining (*endometrium*)

cervix

vagina

The women's internal sex organs. The diagram shows the womb and vagina in longitudinal section (as though cut in half).

course, or around a baby during labour. The walls of the vagina normally touch each other: it doesn't stay permanently open like a piece of plastic pipe.

When a girl or woman gets sexually excited, the vaginal opening and the walls of the vagina become very moist and the vagina opens up and gets bigger. This means that when a couple have intercourse the man's penis can slip into the woman's vagina more easily and comfortably.

When a doctor needs to check a woman's internal sexual organs to make sure they are healthy, he or she can do this by putting two fingers into the vagina and gently pressing down on the outside of the abdomen with the fingers of the other hand. Or a speculum can be used – an instrument which can be slid into the vagina to hold the walls apart so the doctor can see the cervix.

The WOMB (or UTERUS) is about the size and shape of a small upside-down pear. It is about 8 cm (3 in) long and in most women it tilts forwards. It is made of muscle. It is where the baby grows and develops during pregnancy.

The CERVIX is a ring of muscles at the bottom end of the womb where it joins with the vagina. The cervix is also called the NECK OF THE WOMB. It is normally all but closed, with just a tiny opening for blood to pass through during the monthly period. The hole in the cervix is too small for a tampon to pass through, and certainly too small for a penis.

There are two OVARIES, each about the size of an almond. They produce the female cells, the egg cells or OVA. (Ova is the plural: one ovum, two or more ova.) Each ovary contains many thousands of unripe ova. In girls who have reached puberty, and in women, one

49

ovum ripens every month and moves from the ovary into the fallopian tube. This is called OVULATION (see page 72). If the ripe ovum is then fertilized by a man's sperm, it will make a new cell which will develop into a baby (see page 99).

The ovaries also produce the female sex hormones,

The woman's sex organs, seen from the side. All the organs except the fallopian tube and ovary are shown in longitudinal section (as though cut in half).

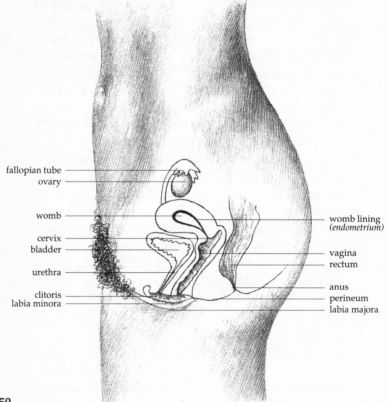

fallopian tube
ovary

womb

cervix
bladder

urethra

clitoris
labia minora

womb lining
(*endometrium*)

vagina
rectum

anus
perineum
labia majora

OESTROGEN and PROGESTERONE. These hormones cause some of the changes which take place during the menstrual cycle (see pages 72 to 73).

The FALLOPIAN TUBES lead from the ovaries to the womb. Where the fallopian tube meets the ovary, there is a fringe-like structure which 'catches' the ovum as it leaves the ovary.

The ENDOMETRIUM is the lining of the womb. This is shed in the monthly period (see pages 72 to 73) and a new lining is made.

 THE MALE SEX ORGANS

The PENIS is used for urinating and also for sexual inter-course and lovemaking. Penises vary a lot in size. A grown man's penis can be anything from about 3.5 to 10 cm (1½–4 in) long when it is limp, and from about 9 to 20 cm (3½–8 in) when it is erect. The size of a penis has nothing to do with how well it works or how 'sexy' a man is. Smaller penises tend to enlarge more when they become erect, and bigger penises tend to enlarge less.

The end of the penis is covered by a sheath of skin called the FORESKIN. A baby's foreskin can't usually be pulled back, but as a boy grows older the foreskin becomes looser and can be pulled back to show the tip of the penis underneath. This smooth rounded tip is called the GLANS. Glans is the Latin word for acorn – which is rather what the uncovered end of the penis looks like.

Adolescent boys who haven't been circumcised need to make sure they pull the foreskin back to wash underneath it. Otherwise a whitish, waxy substance called SMEGMA can collect under the foreskin and can become smelly and infected. Smegma is produced by

51

glands underneath the foreskin and helps the skin slide back smoothly over the tip of the penis when a boy or man has an erection.

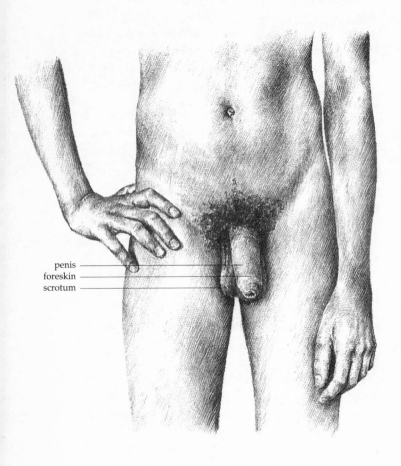

penis
foreskin
scrotum

If a boy or a man has not been circumcised, the end of the penis is
covered by a sheath of skin called the foreskin.

It is the custom in some cultures and religions to cut off the foreskin. This is called CIRCUMCISION. Sometimes circumcision is carried out for medical reasons, for

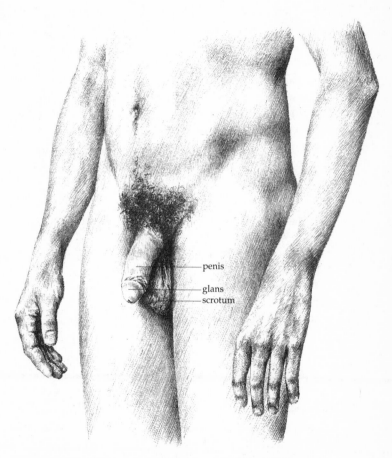

penis

glans
scrotum

A circumcised penis (with the foreskin removed) looks different because you can see the glans (the rounded tip of the penis).

53

example to prevent infection. A circumcised penis looks different to an uncircumcised one but they work exactly the same.

Inside the penis is a tube called the URETHRA. Both urine (from the bladder) and sperm (from the testes) pass out of the penis down this tube. Urine and sperm cannot pass out at the same time.

The SCROTUM is the bag of skin which hangs down behind the penis. It contains the testes, where sperm are made. The scrotum helps to keep the testes at a constant temperature, just below that of the rest of the body. This is necessary because sperm can't develop at body temperature. When it is hot, the scrotum hangs down lower, away from the body, to keep the testes cool. When it is cold, the scrotum pulls up closer to the body for warmth.

There are two TESTES (or TESTICLES), each about the size of a small plum. (Testes is the plural: one testis, two testes.) The testis on the left side usually hangs down lower in the scrotum than the one on the right. Inside the testes is a mass of fine tubes – three-quarters of a mile of coiled tube in each testis. This is where sperm are made. The testes also produce the male sex hormone TESTOSTERONE which causes the changes in a boy's body at puberty (see page 65).

SPERM are the male cells which can fertilize a female cell (an ovum) to make a baby. Sperm are very small – about one twentieth of a millimetre long – so they can only be seen under a microscope. They have a head, middle piece and tail and, once they are fully mature, they are able to swim by moving the tail from side to side. Many millions of sperm are produced in the testes – about 100 million every 24 hours in an adult man. A boy starts to produce sperm during puberty (see pages 65 and 70).

Sperm pass from the testis into the EPIDIDYMIS. This

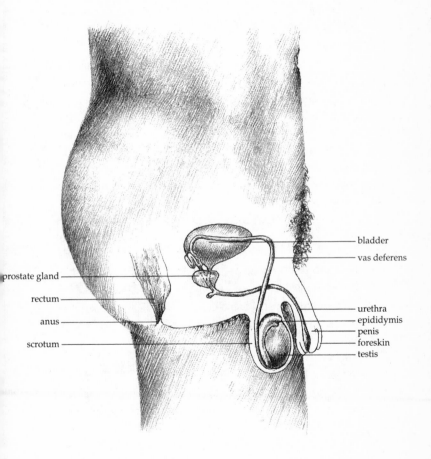

prostate gland

rectum

anus

scrotum

bladder

vas deferens

urethra

epididymis

penis

foreskin

testis

The man's internal sex organs, seen from the side.

55

is a coiled tube lying over the back of each testis. They then move up into the **VAS DEFERENS**, the tube leading from each testis into the urethra. When a man ejaculates,

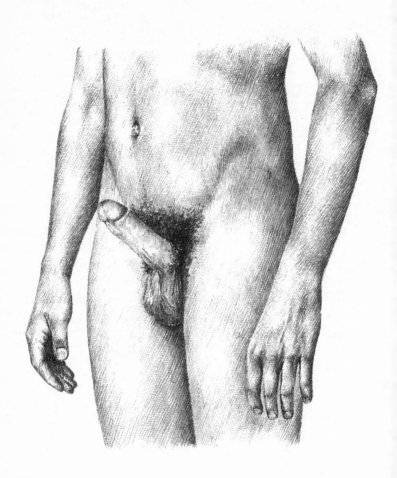

An erect penis. The angle of the erection can vary.

the prostate and other glands add secretions to the sperm to make SEMEN, which spurts out from the end of the penis.

Sperm don't *have* to be ejaculated. If they aren't used, the sperm simply break up and disappear.

ERECTIONS mostly happen when a man or boy is thinking about sex, or when he, or someone else, touches and stimulates his penis. But erections can also happen for no obvious reason and at any time. Sometimes this is embarrassing, although nobody really notices as much as the owner of the erect penis thinks they do. Thinking hard about something *not* to do with sex usually makes the erection go away again quite quickly. Often erections happen at night, during sleep, and it's fairly common to wake in the morning with an erect penis.

A man's penis has to be erect for him to have sexual intercourse (see page 84).

An ERECTION is when the penis becomes stiff and stands up. The penis is made from special tissue (called ERECTILE TISSUE) which acts like a sponge. When the tissue fills with blood, the penis becomes larger and erect. Boys have erections from babyhood onwards but they happen more often during puberty.

PUBERTY

TALKING ABOUT PUBERTY

◆ Children cope much better with the physical and emotional changes of puberty if they feel prepared and know what to expect. Having a period or a wet dream for the first time without knowing what is happening or how to cope can be really distressing. So it's important to talk to children about puberty *before it begins* – before they're about nine or ten years old.

◆ It's quite difficult to explain clearly all the changes connected with puberty and it can't be done in one go. If you start with just the basic information, then you can pick the subject up again and add more later. You'll need to talk every now and then over a period of time and be ready to answer questions.

◆ When you talk, try to be positive. It's easy to make growing up seem very problematic and not much fun – especially for girls. Try to look at what's good about growing up, and at the same time be clear that you'll be there to help if there are any problems or difficulties.

◆ In some families, conversations about sex tend to happen between fathers and sons, and between mothers and daughters. But sex is really a shared concern. So although a girl will naturally ask her mother rather than her father about period pains or how to put in a tampon, and a boy will probably ask his father rather than his mother about what an ejaculation is like or what to do about untimely erections, it's helpful if both parents can talk about *every* aspect of sex and sexuality. Fathers may not be able to talk in detail about periods or other 'female' topics, but they can show that they understand the basics and that they're not embarrassed by the subject. The same goes for mothers and 'male' topics. In one-parent families it's especially important that the parent can talk about both male and female issues, and maybe also finds someone of the opposite sex to help. (See pages 145 to 147 for more on avoiding sexism in sex education.)

◆ Puberty can be a difficult, stressful time for children (not to mention their parents). There are physical changes, emotional changes, and changes in relationships both inside and outside the family. There are tensions and often a lot of arguments. Some children feel awkward, self-conscious or insecure; many swing between feeling excited and happy one moment, down and depressed the next. Friendships become very important, either within a gang or one-to-one, and a child who feels left out or hasn't got a special friend (of either sex) can feel very lonely. For all these reasons it's important for parents and children to talk and to keep talking, not just about physical change but also about what it feels like to be moving gradually into adulthood.

As children get older, it sometimes becomes

more difficult for them to talk to their parents, and more difficult for their parents to talk to them. Some teenagers talk more easily with an adult outside their immediate family, or even someone who isn't close to them – such as a teacher. Parents need to keep this in mind and be prepared to hand over to other people sometimes if this seems to help.

- - - -

◆ Before you explain puberty to your children, give some thought to the words you are going to use. Children need to know the proper words – erection, ejaculation, menstruation and so on – but you may also want to use other words, either because you feel easier with them, or because they are words that children are bound to come across and are more likely to use themselves. For example, you may want to use the word 'come' as well as 'ejaculate', or 'hard on' as well as 'erection'. (There's more about the language of sex on pages 23 to 27.)

- - - -

◆ The Book List on pages 165–167 includes books and booklets written for children and teenagers about puberty.

PUBERTY: WHAT CHILDREN NEED TO KNOW

WHAT HAPPENS AND HOW TO COPE

Children need clear, factual information about the physical changes that puberty brings and how to cope with them. And they need this information before the changes start happening. For girls especially, it makes life much easier if they know in advance how to cope with periods. So have supplies of sanitary towels ready and waiting and talk together about how to use them. Lots of detailed, practical information can really help and is very reassuring.

Boys and girls need the same basic information about what happens during puberty. Boys should know about periods, for example, and girls about wet dreams, and each also needs to have some understanding of the feelings that might accompany these events.

HOW IT FEELS

Puberty is more than just physical development. Children also have to cope with changes in their feelings and relationships and often it's not easy. They need to be aware that puberty is a time when they grow in every possible way. Knowing that this is accepted by everyone in the family does help, even if there are still disputes (as there usually are) about growing independence.

WHAT IT MEANS TO BE MALE OR FEMALE

In the time around puberty, children gradually become more aware of the differences between the sexes, and it's important to talk about differences besides the

61

physical ones. One way of doing this is to look at what is truly and obviously different (for example, women have breasts and men don't) and then to question other differences that are either assumed (for example, girls play with dolls but boys don't), or imposed by society (for example, boys ask girls out but girls don't ask boys). See Sexism pages 50 to 53 for more about this and some suggestions about how to help children think and understand about sex differences and gender roles.

⸻ LIKING YOURSELF, FEELING CONFIDENT ⸻

Children gradually become much more aware of their bodies and sometimes this leads to all kinds of worries and dissatisfactions. Teenagers are often anxious about their appearance. They worry about the size of their feet, their breasts, their bottom, their genitals. . . . They worry about the shape of their legs, the style of their hair, their height (or lack of it), and the amount of body hair they are (or aren't) growing. They know how they would *like* to look (usually like the models in magazines) and, if they don't measure up to their ideal, they often feel very negative about themselves and their own bodies. On top of this, most become spotty at some stage during puberty and no one feels particularly happy about that.

It's hard to help with these sorts of worries. You can't change the way your child looks. But you *can* try to help your child feel positive about him or herself, with or without big feet, nose or bottom, by endorsing what you know they like about themselves, even if they never admit it. You can also help your child to be critical of the stereotypical images that the media promote, especially in teenage magazines. Knowing about the power of the media won't prevent your child from being affected by it, but it may help to keep things in proportion. For more about this, see Sex in the Media pages 140 to 144 and Pressures and Choices pages 153 to 157.

Girls sometimes worry about the size and shape of their breasts. There are times when breasts are fashionable and times when they're not. It's hard if you happen to be flat-chested at a time when breasts are thought to be attractive, or if you have large breasts when all the clothes in the shops are made for girls who hardly have any breasts at all. For boys, there's sometimes a similar kind of worry about the size of their penis – they may think it isn't big enough, for example, or doesn't look like other boys' penises. Often this is because a penis looks smaller to its owner than it does to other people. Looking down on a penis makes it seem smaller, and other people's penises look bigger and different because you see them from a different angle. The fact is that penises are all shapes and sizes, and size has nothing at all to do with how well they work. Any size of penis, circumcised or uncircumcised, can become erect and give pleasure.

Children who start puberty particularly early or late may need extra reassurance. For a girl, being an early developer can be especially hard. She may be embarrassed about being taller than her friends, having more developed breasts or a more curvy body, or having started periods. If she looks mature, teachers and other adults may treat her as older than she is and expect her to cope with more than she really can. She may attract attention from boys and men that she doesn't want or doesn't know how to respond to. And if her friends aren't going through similar difficulties, then she won't have anyone to talk to about it all. For boys, it's more of a problem to be a late developer. They can easily feel left out, especially if they mix with a group of boys who act tough and are physically much stronger than they are.

PUBERTY: THE FACTS

PHYSICAL CHANGES

Puberty is the change from childhood to adulthood. It's a gradual change that usually takes two to five years.

Physically, some children start to develop early, some late, and a lot in between. There's nothing significant about this: it's just the way people are. A few girls will have their first period as early as nine or ten years old, others not until they are 15 or older. Boys generally start puberty later than girls – usually between the ages of about 11 and 17.

Puberty begins when the HYPOTHALAMUS, a part of the brain, triggers the production of new hormones. HORMONES are chemicals that circulate in the blood and carry 'messages' from one part of the body to another. There are many different hormones involved in the development of the body during puberty. Some are produced by the PITUITARY GLAND, which is a gland at the base of the brain; others are produced by the ovaries (in a girl) and testes (in a boy). At puberty, a girl's ovaries begin to produce the hormones OESTROGEN and PROGESTERONE; and a boy's testes begin to produce TESTOSTERONE. These hormones bring about the various physical changes of adolescence.

64

CHANGES IN BOYS

In boys, the first sign of puberty is usually that the testes and then the penis get bigger, and the scrotum darkens and becomes more wrinkled. The testes start to produce sperm. Erections happen more often, and ejaculation and wet dreams start (see page 70). Hair grows on the face (usually starting on the upper lip), under the arms and around the genitals, and there's more hair on the body generally. Some boys find that their breasts get bigger for a while – then go down again after about a year. The larynx, or voice box, grows, causing the voice to break. The voice may sound odd for a while before it deepens. Muscles get bigger and stronger. The skin sweats more and becomes greasier. Often this causes spots and other skin problems, but these usually clear up (or at least lessen) after puberty.

Boys, like girls, have a growth spurt at puberty, but it happens later, round about the age of 12 or later.

EJACULATIONS AND WET DREAMS

An EJACULATION is when semen spurts out from the opening at the end of the penis. Semen is a fluid that contains sperm (see pages 54 to 57). Ejaculation can happen when a boy masturbates (pages 80 and 86), during sexual intercourse (pages 83 to 85), or during sleep (see wet dreams page 70).

In one ejaculation there is about one teaspoonful of semen and, in that teaspoonful, there may be around 300 million sperm. When a boy first starts to ejaculate, the semen is usually clear; later it is milky and thick. Usually the penis has to be erect before ejaculation happens, but boys and men don't ejaculate every time they have an erection.

*How the body develops, from child to adult.
Everybody develops at a different rate.*

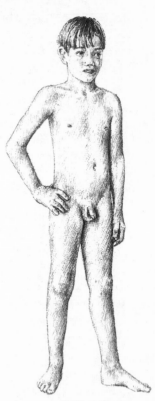

　　　　　2–3 years　　　　　　　　　　　7–10 years

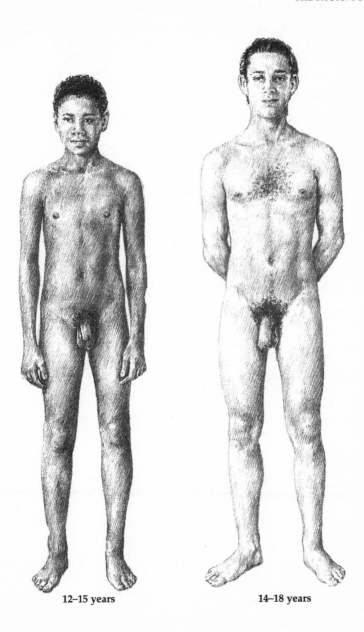

12–15 years   14–18 years   67

How the body develops from child to adult.
Everybody develops at a different rate.
Girls' changes usually happen earlier than boys'.

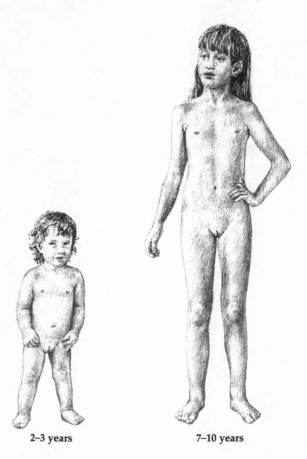

2–3 years   **7–10 years**

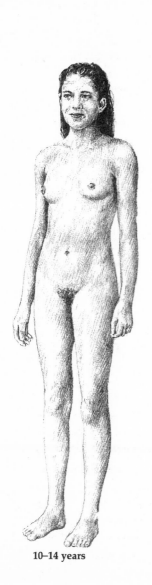

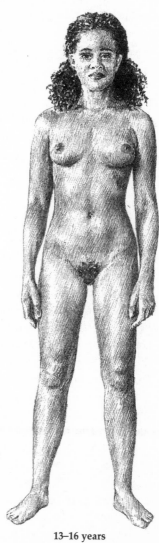

10–14 years   13–16 years

WET DREAMS are ejaculations of sperm that happen while a man or boy is asleep. They can happen with or without an erection. Sometimes the ejaculation happens as part of a dream about something sexual and goes along with pleasant sexual feelings; sometimes the ejaculation happens for no apparent reason.

Wet dreams usually start when a boy is about 14 years old or earlier. At puberty, the testes begin to produce sperm for the first time and other glands begin to produce the fluids that make up semen. Wet dreams are the way in which the body 'practises' ejaculating sperm and semen.

 CHANGES IN GIRLS

Usually the first sign of puberty in girls is that they start to grow much faster. This growth spurt happens earlier in girls than in boys – around the ages of ten to twelve. Next, the breasts develop: they stand out more and become rounder and fuller. They may be a bit tender at first and often they are uneven in size. The nipples also start to stand out more and get darker in colour. Hair grows under the arms and also low on the abdomen and around the vulva (pubic hair). There is more hair on face, arms and legs, but this is less noticeable. The voice deepens a little. Hips become wider and the body rounder. The womb and vagina get bigger, and the genitals (the labia and clitoris) become fleshier and more sensitive. The ovaries start to produce ova and periods start (see page 71). The skin sweats more and becomes greasier. Often this causes spots and other skin problems, but these usually clear up (or at least lessen) once puberty is over.

70

 MENSTRUATION

Most girls start to menstruate (have periods) some-where between the ages of 12 and 14, although some start much earlier and some much later.

Having a period means losing blood from the womb through the vagina. Sometimes the blood that is lost at the first period is more brown than red. Periods usually happen about every 28 days, but for the first year or so they may happen less often and they may be irregular.

The bleeding is part of a pattern of events called the MENSTRUAL CYCLE that happens every month from puberty until a woman is in her forties or fifties. ('Menstrual' means 'monthly'.) It is the body's system for preparing for conception (see page 97) and, if a baby is *not* conceived, for cleaning the womb.

Girls and women vary a lot in the length of their menstrual cycle, the length of their periods, how regular they are, and how much they bleed. A 28-day cycle (as shown in the chart on pages 72–73) is the average, but cycles can range from 20 to 36 days. Bleeding can last from two to eight days.

When they start to menstruate or maybe just before, some girls find they also start to lose a little whitish fluid from the vagina. This fluid is produced in the vagina to keep it moist and healthy. The amount of fluid that's produced varies from one girl, or one woman, to the next. Most girls and women get used to the amount that's usual for them. The amount of vaginal fluid produced also increases with sexual excitement.

The menstrual cycle is controlled by two main hormones, oestrogen and progesterone. The levels of these hormones change during the cycle. The hormonal

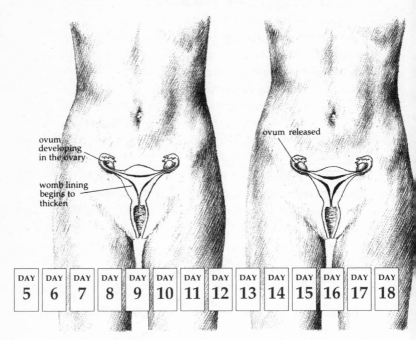

DAY 5	DAY 6	DAY 7	DAY 8	DAY 9	DAY 10	DAY 11	DAY 12	DAY 13	DAY 14	DAY 15	DAY 16	DAY 17	DAY 18

This chart shows a 28-day cycle. Some girls' and women's cycles are longer, some shorter. Day 1 on the chart is the first day of a period.

THE MENSTRUAL CYCLE

During menstruation (a period) the lining of the womb comes away and is passed out of the vagina. At the same time an ovum, or egg cell, is developing in one of the ovaries.

The hormone oestrogen, which is produced in the ovaries, causes a new womb lining to begin to grow. Gradually the lining gets thicker.

About 14 days before a period is due, an ovum is released from one of the ovaries. This is *ovulation*.

If the ovum is fertilized by a sperm (see Conception, page 103), it will move down into the womb and become implanted in the specially prepared lining.

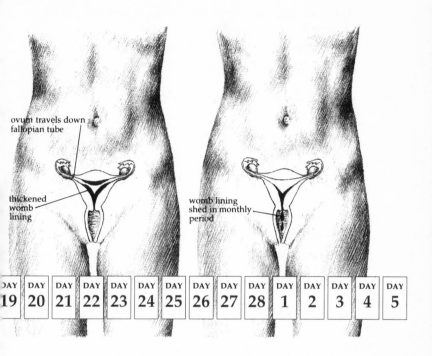

ovum travels down
fallopian tube

thickened
womb
lining

womb lining
shed in monthly
period

DAY 19	DAY 20	DAY 21	DAY 22	DAY 23	DAY 24	DAY 25	DAY 26	DAY 27	DAY 28	DAY 1	DAY 2	DAY 3	DAY 4	DAY 5

The ovum travels down the fallopian tube. The ovaries now produce a second hormone, progesterone. The progesterone brings about further changes to the womb lining, making it ready to receive a fertilized egg cell.

If the egg cell is not fertilized, the womb lining breaks down and is passed out of the vagina along with some blood. At the same time, a new ovum is beginning to ripen in one of the ovaries – and the cycle begins again.

73

changes which take place during the menstrual cycle sometimes bring physical symptoms. For example, some girls find they get swollen and tender breasts, or greasy skin and hair, immediately before a period. A lot also find that their menstrual cycle affects them emotionally. Many feel tense and irritable just before a period.

For some girls and women, periods bring problems. These can include painful cramps low down in their abdomen, headaches, feeling very heavy and bloated, or very down and depressed. When symptoms like these occur regularly before every period it is called PMS, or premenstrual syndrome. Other girls and women have very heavy or long or irregular periods. Often these kinds of problems can be eased through self-help – exercise and relaxation, for example, can help with period pains and PMS. But sometimes it's

Different kinds of sanitary towels suit different girls and women.

sensible to see a doctor, who may be able to help with specialist advice on painkillers, for example, or, very occasionally, with hormone treatment.

 SANITARY TOWELS AND TAMPONS

A **SANITARY TOWEL** is a soft pad worn in the pants to soak up the blood that is lost during a period. Most types of towel have a sticky strip that holds it in place.

A **TAMPON** is a small, tight roll of cotton wool with a string at one end. It is put into the vagina and soaks up the blood that is lost during a period. The tampon is taken out by pulling the string.

Some tampons are just pushed into the vagina, using a finger. Others have an applicator – a cardboard tube that helps to push the tampon into place.

Putting in a tampon (see page 76).

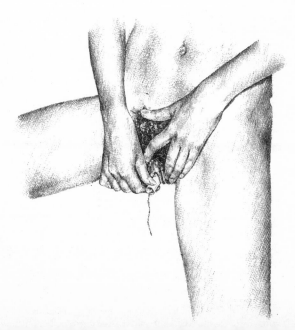

Tampons and sanitary towels come in different sizes to cope with lighter or heavier bleeding. There are special slender tampons for girls just starting their periods.

Most girls need a bit of practice before they can put in a tampon easily. It helps to know that:

- it's impossible to put a tampon into the urethra instead of the vagina.
- once the tampon is in the right place, high up in the vagina, it can't be felt.
- it's impossible to push the tampon in too far, or for it to get lost inside. Even if the string gets lost, the tampon can always be reached and can be pulled out using the fingers. Squatting, or putting one foot up on a chair or the loo seat, makes this easier.

It's important to change tampons regularly and not leave them in too long.

A tampon in place. When it's in the right place, high up in the vagina it can't be felt.

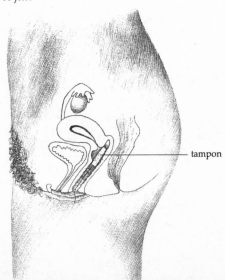

tampon

SEX

TALKING ABOUT SEX

◆ Trying to describe sexual intercourse to a child of any age is no easy task ('But how do you *do* it, Mum?'). No matter how carefully you choose your words, the activity often ends up sounding silly – or downright hilarious ('You must be *joking*!').

One trap for parents when they tackle the subject is that they can find themselves describing their own lovemaking, even though they are saying 'The man and the woman . . .' This makes the whole conversation much more awkward and uncomfortable. Try to talk about people in general rather than you in particular. The wording given on pages 83 to 85 may help you.

◆ The language you use is important. Try to use words that aren't aggressive. For example, try to describe the penis as being 'slipped' into the vagina rather than 'pushed' and to talk about the vagina as stretchy emphasizing the wetness that helps the penis go into the vagina easily.

It's also important to use words like 'loving', 'caring', 'feeling good', 'kissing', 'caressing', and to emphasize feelings and each partner's consideration for the other. Describing sexual intercourse in a purely mechanical way may be easier, but it doesn't give children any real idea of what the whole thing is about. For more on this see pages 17 to 20.

◆ One of the biggest difficulties for parents can be knowing how much information to give to their children at what age. There's some guidance about this (see 'Sex: What Children Need to Know' opposite), and there's more help on pages 10 to 13. You'll need to think it over and make your own decisions but, whatever you decide, try to work out what you feel will help your child most, and try not to let any of your own feelings of embarrassment, or reluctance, get in the way. (See pages 21 to 25 for ways of getting over embarrassment.) You will also need to be flexible, because although you may make a firm decision not to talk about something until your child is older, you may find that you're unexpectedly faced with a question on precisely the topic you'd decided not to talk about. It's important then to respond in an honest, informative way even if what you say is very limited.

―――

◆ Remember that children learn about sex from lots of different sources besides their parents – from friends, from school (both in the classroom and in the playground), from the media, from books. Some of the information they get hold of in this way will be useful to them, but some may be inaccurate, unhelpful or even worrying. So it's important whenever you talk about sex, no matter what age your child is, to make time and opportunities for lots of questions and for two-way conversation. Then you can set the record straight, or reassure, depending on what is needed.

SEX: WHAT CHILDREN NEED TO KNOW

================ SEX AS LOVEMAKING AND PLEASURE ================

Almost all children first learn about sexual intercourse as reproduction. They ask questions like 'Where do babies come from?' or 'Where did I come from?' long before they ask questions about sex. And parents on the whole find it easier to explain sexual intercourse as a part of making babies. But in time, children need to learn that sex is also for pleasure and can be an expression of love and part of a loving relationship *without* producing a baby. Most children learn this gradually, taking it in bit by bit, but they also need it to be explained to them directly.

================ PRIVACY ================

Children need to understand early on that sex is a private part of people's lives. Many parents worry that explaining sexual intercourse to children will make them curious about what parents do together in bed. One father who carefully described lovemaking to his son was met with the request, 'Can I come and watch?'. Although at first the father wasn't sure how to reply, in the end he simply explained that sex is something which adults do in private when no one is watching or with them.

Children also need to learn that it isn't acceptable (for the simple reason that it's bad manners) to ask people about their sex lives; and that sex is something that isn't, on the whole, discussed in public. You have to try to get across the idea that sex is private *without* suggesting that it's something so embarrassing that it can never be spoken of at all. Parents often go through a few embarrassing experiences before their children understand this.

SEX AND RELATIONSHIPS

Children need to understand that sex usually takes place within a relationship and that it is one way that people express their feelings for each other. Later, this can lead to an understanding of different kinds of relationships, both heterosexual and homosexual, and different ways of loving. Equally, children need to understand that a loving relationship doesn't have to be sexual.

Some parents will want to say that sex should *only* take place within a strong, loving, well-established relationship (which for some will mean marriage). Others will put less emphasis on this, perhaps simply saying that sex should happen within a caring relationship, whatever kind of relationship that may be.

MASTURBATION

Masturbation is the one form of sex which can take place outside a relationship as well as within one. There is a very wide range of opinion and feeling about it. Some parents will want to explain it as a natural, normal activity, saying that it can be pleasurable but should only be done in private. Others, especially those with religious beliefs which forbid masturbation, may find it difficult to talk about masturbation in anything but negative terms. But it's important to remember that many children do masturbate, often unconsciously,

80

and it's possible to make a child feel very guilty and unhappy about doing this. Often children feel very relieved when they are told that masturbation is natural, allowable, and part of discovering your body's sexual responses. What's more, it is widespread among both girls and boys. (See page 86 for more information.)

HOMOSEXUALITY

Children's understanding of sexuality develops very gradually. From the start, part of that understanding should be that people have different sexual identities and choose different kinds of sexual behaviour. In particular, children need to know what it means to be homosexual. This applies equally to children who have some experience of homosexuality within their family as well as to children who only have contact with heterosexuals.

A huge amount of prejudice still exists around homosexuality and children need to be aware of this and of what it can mean in the lives of individual homosexuals or lesbians. They need to learn that there is thought to be a wide spectrum of sexual feelings, ranging from people who are exclusively heterosexual to those who are exclusively homosexual. Many people come somewhere in between. (See pages 88 to 89 for more information.)

THE RIGHT TO SAY NO

It's vital that children learn that everyone has the right to choose whether or not they have sex with someone else; and that no one should be forced, in any way at all,

81

to have sex when they don't want it or in a way that they don't want. This is essential information. It gives children some understanding of, and protection against, abuse, and it sets a proper value on sex and sexual relationships.

You may like to go over with your child what they should do if they are approached by anyone, molested, or interfered with in any way. This isn't easy to do, but it can be very reassuring for children, and for parents too. For more about this, see pages 157 to 159.

This is just one of the many positions for intercourse.

SEX: THE FACTS

SEXUAL INTERCOURSE

For a man and woman to enjoy sexual intercourse, they need to know that they trust and care for each other. Also they must both want to have sex.

They will take time beforehand to show each other how they feel and to excite each other sexually. They will probably kiss, touch, stroke and rub each other.

Taking time over this first part of making love is important. It's enjoyable and brings people close. It helps the woman in particular to feel ready for intercourse.

As a man becomes sexually excited, his penis becomes erect and hard. When a woman becomes sexually excited her vagina and vulva become very moist, and her vagina opens up and gets bigger. Her clitoris becomes firm and stands up more.

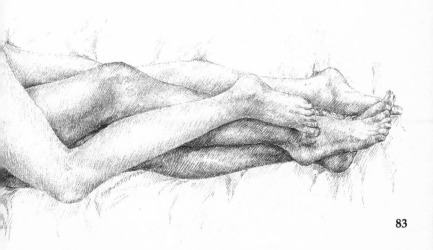

When both the man and woman feel ready, the man slips his erect penis into the woman's vagina. Because the vagina is moist, large, and very stretchy, it isn't usually difficult for the man to slide his penis inside.

The man moves his penis backwards and forwards inside the woman's vagina. The woman moves her hips and squeezes the man's penis by tightening the muscles around her vagina. Both partners may go on kissing and caressing each other. Experienced couples can make this part of lovemaking last for quite a long time and will gradually become more and more sexually excited.

This diagram shows how the man's penis fits inside the woman's vagina during sexual intercourse.

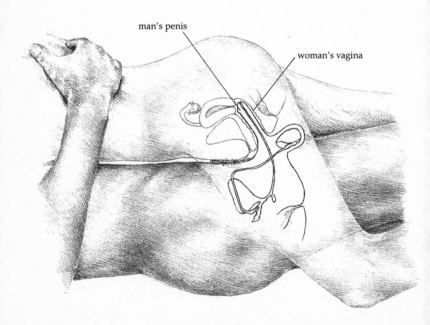

man's penis

woman's vagina

Finally, both the man and the woman may reach a climax – that is, have an orgasm, or 'come'. They don't always have an orgasm at the same time. When the man has an orgasm, he ejaculates (see page 65). A woman may need to have her clitoris gently stimulated before she reaches her orgasm.

For both men and women, an orgasm brings a feeling which no one can quite describe – a warm, throbbing, relaxing feeling which spreads through the whole body. A man usually reaches just one climax; a woman may have one or several. A lot depends on the way a couple make love.

After orgasm, some couples like to go on loving and caressing each other; others like to rest and relax. The man may take his penis out of the woman's vagina (and he *must* take it out if he is using a condom – see pages 115 to 117), or he will wait until his penis goes soft and then it will simply slip out.

People have sex in all kinds of different positions. When a couple know each other well and have made love a number of times, they begin to learn which positions suit them best. The 'missionary position' is a position that many couples use. It is called this because people in the South Sea Islands, who used to make love sitting up and face to face, were told by a European missionary that the 'right' way to make love was lying down with the man on top. In fact, there's no 'right' way and some couples much prefer the woman to be on top or to be in a position where neither partner is on top, such as lying on their sides, sitting or kneeling.

THE LAW ON SEX

Under the 1956 Sexual Offences Act, it is against the law in England, Scotland and Wales for a man (or a boy over 14 years old) to have sexual intercourse with a girl who is under 16 (under 17 in Northern Ireland).

Under the 1967 Sexual Offences Act, homosexual acts (which the law defines as buggery or gross indecency) are against the law unless carried out in private between men who both give their consent and are over the age of 21.

Under the 1956 Sexual Offences Act, it is against the law for anyone to make an indecent assault on another person. It is not against the law if the person concerned consents, but a boy or girl under 16 cannot in law give consent.

MASTURBATION

The majority of small children masturbate quite naturally because it feels nice and it's comforting. Later on, masturbation is the way that lots of young people learn for the first time what sex is like. And for young people and adults alike, it's one way of having 'safer sex' (see pages 137 to 138).

Masturbation is certainly not harmful, as some people have suggested in the past. It used to be said, for example, that masturbation could cause blindness or insanity. Presumably these stories were put about by people who disapproved of masturbation. If the stories were true, there would certainly be a great many blind, insane people around.

Masturbation means rubbing the sex organs in a way that feels good and may bring about an orgasm. Boys and men usually masturbate by rubbing the penis up and down until they ejaculate. Girls and women usually stroke the area around the clitoris, and rub the clitoris itself. Everyone does what feels good for them – there's no single way that's guaranteed to be good for everyone.

Boys are more likely to masturbate than girls. They are used to touching their penises: they have to every time they urinate. Most can also reach a climax fairly quickly and this may encourage them to masturbate. A girl doesn't *have* to touch herself very much, and she may take longer to reach a climax. But masturbating can help a girl discover what kind of touching she likes, and it teaches her what an orgasm is like. This can be helpful for her in sexual relationships later on.

Boys often try to masturbate very quickly – maybe because they feel guilty about doing it, or because they worry that someone will find them. But it is better for boys to take time over masturbating and to learn how they can prolong the build-up towards an orgasm. This may help them in later sexual relationships.

ORAL SEX

Oral sex is sex using the mouth. The partners caress and stimulate each other using their mouths and tongues. This includes stimulating a woman's labia and clitoris, or a man's penis. Each partner may reach an orgasm. If a man ejaculates into his partner's mouth, the semen is either swallowed or spat out. Swallowing semen isn't harmful, and it can't make a woman pregnant. (Some children may be confused about this.)

It is possible to pass on sexually transmitted diseases by having oral sex (see pages 128 to 132).

Some people find the idea of oral sex unacceptable or shocking. For many others, it is normal, natural and enjoyable. For some people who are physically disabled, it is the only way they have of giving or receiving sexual pleasure, so for them it is very important. Oral sex can also play a part in homosexual relationships.

HOMOSEXUALITY

A homosexual is someone who is sexually attracted to people of their own sex. A homosexual can be a man or a woman: 'homo' comes from the Greek meaning 'the same', not from the Latin for 'man'. A homosexual woman is also called a lesbian. Some people prefer to use the word 'gay' rather than 'homosexual' because it takes the emphasis off sex.

A heterosexual is someone who is sexually attracted to people of the opposite sex. A bisexual is someone who is sexually attracted to both men and women.

Homosexuality is as natural as heterosexuality, but less usual. It is thought that between 5 and 10 per cent of the population is homosexual. In the UK that's at least three million people.

Research seems to indicate that people are homosexual without being aware of it from a very early age, as early as five or maybe even two years old. But it can take a long time for people to realize their sexual orientation, especially in the face of social pressure and prejudice. See Learning about Sexuality, page 145.

Just as in heterosexual relationships, sex may or may not be an important part of a homosexual relationship. Each relationship is different. Some homosexual partners make love by kissing, holding, caressing and masturbating each other. Some use oral sex. Male homosexuals may have anal sex.

Anal sex is sexual intercourse in which the penis is put into the anus, or back passage, instead of the vagina. Anal intercourse is illegal for heterosexuals but legal for consenting men over 21 years old, if done in private. Sexually transmitted infections can be passed on by having anal sex (see pages 128 to 132). There is also a risk that it will damage the sphincter muscles – the muscles around the anus.

Some children grow up with a better and closer understanding of homosexuality than most because their parents, or one of their parents, is homosexual. Some men and women only discover their homosexuality after having children within a heterosexual relationship. They may then continue to live with their heterosexual partner, or they may continue to care for their children but within a new, homosexual relationship. Some lesbian women choose to have a child, either conceived heterosexually or by artificial insemination.

TACKLING PREJUDICE

- You can't tell whether someone is homosexual by the way they look.
- Homosexual males are not all camp, lesbians are not all butch.
- Homosexuality is just a normal variation of human sexuality. Homosexuals may be a minority in society but they are not an abnormal minority.
- Homosexuality is not 'catching'. Neither talking about it nor experience of it can turn a true heterosexual into a homosexual nor a true homosexual into a heterosexual.
- Homosexuals have no more interest in young boys or girls than heterosexuals have. There is no association between homosexuality and child abuse. People who have a sexual interest in young children are called paedophiles. This is completely different from homosexuality.

BABIES: CONCEPTION, PREGNANCY AND BIRTH

TALKING ABOUT BABIES

◆ Most children begin to think and wonder about how babies are made and where they come from when they're still very young. Often the arrival of another baby in the family, or in a friend's family, prompts questions. Or they notice pregnant women in the shops or the street and ask for explanations ('Why is that lady so fat?' Or, more embarrassingly if the person concerned is *not* pregnant, 'Is that fat lady going to have a baby?').

But although children want information, the facts about conception, pregnancy and birth are quite complicated and difficult to take in. So at first children need simple (but truthful and accurate) explanations which will allow them to build up their knowledge and understanding gradually. You'll probably need to go over the same ground many times, and each time you can add in new ideas. It's important to let the subject come up naturally, not to make too much of it (or too little), and to keep on talking.

◆ It's probably *not* a good idea to approach the subject by describing reproduction in animals. One seven year old who saw elephants mating at the zoo was afterwards given a clear, detailed explanation of how babies (elephant babies) are conceived. Having listened carefully, she commented: 'I wonder how humans do it?' When

91

she was told that humans do it 'the same way', she laughed and didn't believe it. It's not as easy as it may seem to relate what happens in animals to what happens in human beings. It's not unusual for children to see animals or insects mating and they usually ask what's happening. So an answer is needed which explains what the animals are doing but doesn't confuse the animal activity with the human one.

If children *do* associate animal and human behaviour, then they may think that humans always mate like animals, with the male mounting the female from behind. It's easier for children to think of sexual intercourse as a development of face-to-face hugging and kissing.

♦ It's always best to use the proper terms and to be aware of other possible meanings. For example, if you say that a baby grows inside its mother's 'tummy', it can sound as though the baby is actually in its mother's stomach. For young children this can seem a perfectly reasonable idea since they often think of a baby as being made out of something the mother has eaten and, if the baby is in the mother's stomach, that also solves the puzzling mystery of how it gets out. There are similar problems with talking about 'eggs' instead of 'egg cells' or 'ova', or talking about 'seed' instead of 'sperm'. It can be hard to imagine an egg as anything other than a hen's egg (complete with shell), while the seeds children are familiar with are usually bought in packets and planted in the garden.

◆ The father's role in conception, pregnancy and birth can easily be ignored and so it's important to include what the father does in any explanation.

◆ Children often get hold of mistaken ideas about reproduction, so it's probably worth checking from time to time how much they understand. You may need to talk over some of the things they have been told by others or have made up for themselves. For example:

- a woman *doesn't* swallow the man's semen to make a baby.
- a doctor *doesn't* put the baby inside the mother to grow – and then take it out again when it has grown big enough.
- a baby is *not* made by eating certain foods.
- a baby is *not* born through the navel, or mouth, or anus.
- babies are *not* born by cutting open the mother (except when a Caesarean is needed – see page 109).

◆ Talking about how babies are made can be a lovely experience for both parents and children. There is always plenty of visual material you can use (photos taken during pregnancy, a scan picture, baby photos and so on) and there's usually no difficulty about starting a conversation. Children are often fascinated by what you tell them and it's not difficult to talk reassuringly and positively about the whole process.

Even so, it's sensible to introduce the idea from early on that not all couples can conceive

93

when they want to, and that not all pregnancies succeed. This is realistic and helps to prepare children who may share their parents' distress if a baby miscarries or dies.

Children also need to understand that no one has to have a baby if they don't want to. The idea of *choosing* to have a baby is an important one and reassuring for young children.

◆ The Book List on pages 165–7 includes publications for children on conception, pregnancy and birth.

BABIES: WHAT CHILDREN NEED TO KNOW

HOW BABIES ARE MADE

Even very young children are curious about how babies are made and they need truthful explanations right from the start to help them gradually reach an understanding of the whole complicated process. These are some of the questions young children are likely to ask, and some suggested answers:

Q *Where do babies come from?*
A From inside their mother's womb – a special, safe place inside the mother where the baby can grow. The baby grows inside the mother's womb for about 38 weeks before it is big enough to be born.

Q *How do babies get in?*
A To make a baby, a man's sperm has to join with a woman's ovum (or egg cell). When a man and a woman want to make a baby, the man's penis

becomes hard and the woman's vagina becomes stretchy and large. The man puts his penis into the woman's vagina, and the sperm come out. One sperm joins with the woman's ovum. That is the start of a baby.

––––––––

Q *How does the baby get out?*
A When the baby is ready to be born, it is usually upside-down in the womb. The womb is very muscular and strong and pushes the baby down the vagina and out through the opening between the mother's legs. The vagina and the opening between the legs can stretch until they are big enough for the baby to pass through. When the baby's head appears between its mother's legs, it's a wonderful moment.

All of these answers can be gradually expanded over time to include more detail.

◻◻◻ CONCEPTION, PREGNANCY AND BIRTH ◻◻◻

As children get older, they need to be able to piece together the facts about intercourse, conception, pregnancy and birth to make a complete picture. Gradually they will be able to understand these events as a sequence, happening over a period of time.

Facts about the growth and development of the baby inside the womb can be fascinating for children. Pictures help to explain exactly how the baby grows from the moment of conception onwards. Some books include photos which show what the baby really looks like inside the womb.

95

Children are also interested in details about labour and birth. It is, after all, quite hard to believe that a baby is born in the way that it is, through the vagina, and some children may need convincing about the truth of this information. Children who are *not* given factual information about birth and who have to invent theories of their own, find it hard to think of any hole in the body big enough to let a baby out. It's important to explain how the vagina and the vaginal opening are able to open up wide enough to let the baby through. (However, also see page 109 about Caesareans.)

 PREGNANCY SOMETIMES FAILS

Children need to be aware that all does not always go well during pregnancy or even after the birth of a baby. In the UK, one in five pregnancies end in miscarriage, and over 7000 babies die every year as a stillbirth or in the first weeks of life, so it is dishonest to give the impression that pregnancy is an infallible procedure for producing live, healthy babies. Children can suffer very much when a baby brother or sister dies, or when they see their parents in distress after a miscarriage. Just like their parents, they are better able to accept a loss if they are prepared for the possibility, however remote and however unwanted.

Children also need to understand that a pregnancy is sometimes brought to an end deliberately, either because antenatal tests show that the baby is abnormal, or for other reasons. Children are likely to come across stories about abortion in the media. They need to develop an understanding of this difficult issue and to understand differing views on abortion. (Also see page 109.)

BABIES: THE FACTS

⊏━━━━━━━━━━━━━━⊐ CONCEPTION ⊏━━━━━━━━━━━━━━⊐

A baby is conceived when a woman's ovum is fertilized by a man's sperm. See pages 98 to 99 for an explanation of conception.

It is possible for a woman to conceive at almost any time, including (but extremely rarely) during her period. It is also possible for a woman to conceive without having intercourse. If sperm are put *near* the vagina, some may make their way up to the ovum. But conception is most likely to happen if a couple have intercourse in the days around ovulation – when an ovum is released from one of the woman's ovaries. At this time, hormones cause the mucus in the cervix to become thinner, so the sperm can pass through more easily; and the womb lining becomes thicker, so that it is ready to receive the ovum if it is fertilized.

Sperm can live inside a woman for five days or more. So if a couple have intercourse a few days before the woman ovulates she can still conceive.

CONCEPTION

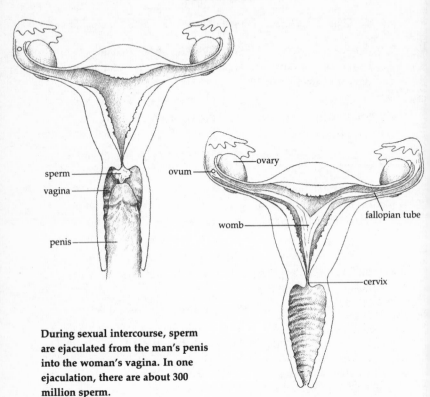

sperm

vagina

penis

ovary

ovum

fallopian tube

womb

cervix

During sexual intercourse, sperm are ejaculated from the man's penis into the woman's vagina. In one ejaculation, there are about 300 million sperm.

Some sperm leak out of the vagina and some die in the acid secretions which are normally produced in the vagina to keep it healthy. But some sperm swim up through the cervix into the womb and on into the fallopian tubes.

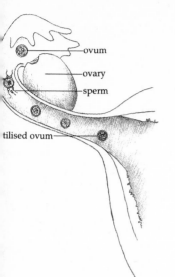

ovum
ovary
sperm
tilised ovum

fertilised ovum
womb
womb lining

If an ovum has been released from one of the woman's ovaries (see page 72), a number of sperm will cluster around it. The ovum releases a chemical which attracts the sperm.

In the next week the fertilized ovum moves down the fallopian tube into the womb. It is already growing. It starts as a single cell, but it divides again and again so that, by the time it reaches the womb, it has become a ball of over 100 cells and is still growing.

Just one sperm, out of all the millions which were ejaculated, eventually joins with the ovum and fertilizes it. The time taken from ejaculation to fertilization is usually no more than an hour or so. Within two weeks of fertilization, the ball of cells attaches itself to the lining of the womb. This is called *implantation*. When implantation has happened, conception is said to have taken place.

99

=============== THE BABY'S SEX ===============

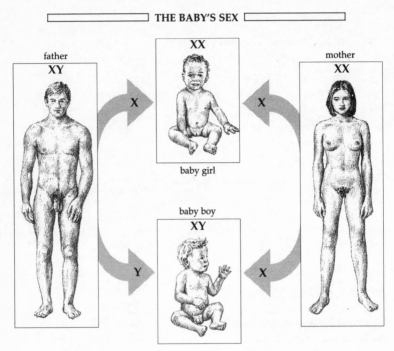

The sex of the baby is decided at the moment of fertilization.

The fertilized ovum contains 46 chromosomes, 23 from the mother and 23 from the father. Chromosomes are tiny, thread-like structures through which characteristics such as hair and eye colour are passed on from parents to children.

There are two sex chromosomes in the fertilized ovum, one from the mother and one from the father. The sex chromosome from the mother is always the same and is called the X chromosome. The sex chromosome from the father's sperm may be X or Y. If the ovum is fertilized by a sperm containing an X chromosome, then the baby is a girl (XX). If the ovum is fertilized by a sperm containing a Y chromosome, the baby is a boy (XY).

100   So it is the father's sperm which determines the baby's sex.

TWINS

In the UK about one in every 100 women gives birth to twins. Twins are either identical or non-identical.

Identical twins are the result of one fertilized ovum splitting into two groups of cells. Each cell group grows into a baby. Because they originally came from the same egg, the babies look alike and are the same sex.

Non-identical twins are more common. They are the result of two ova being fertilized by two sperm at the same time, so the babies aren't necessarily the same sex and they may not look particularly like each other.

PREGNANCY

A baby grows in the womb for about 38 weeks before it is ready to be born. But pregnancy is always counted from the first day of a woman's last period, not from the time that the baby starts to grow. This adds two weeks on to the real length of pregnancy, making it 40 weeks. So when a doctor describes a woman as 'six weeks pregnant', it is probably only about four weeks since she conceived. The illustrations on pages 102 to 103 show how a baby grows in the womb during pregnancy.

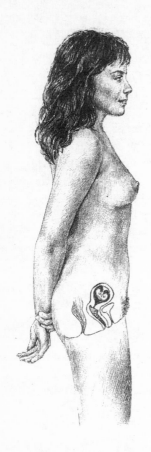

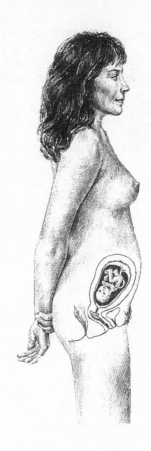

By 12 weeks, a baby is already fully formed inside the womb. It has all its organs, muscles and limbs, and a soft skeleton. But it is still very small – about 5 cm (2 in) long from the top of its head to its bottom. From now on, the baby has to grow and mature.

By 14 to 16 weeks, the baby has a strong heartbeat. The womb is very stretchy and expands around the baby as it grows. The breasts also grow larger.

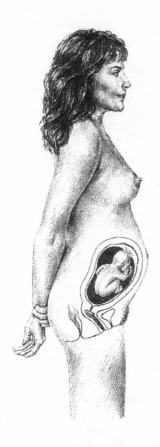

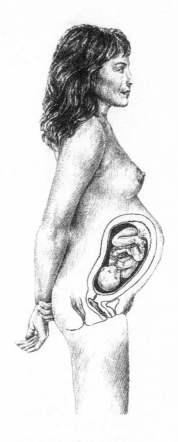

The baby is able to move around inside the womb and at around 18 to 22 weeks the mother can feel the baby moving inside her.

By the end of pregnancy, most babies have settled into a head-down position, ready to be born head first. Just a few are born feet first. At 40 weeks, a baby measures about 45–50 cm (18–20 in) from head to bottom.

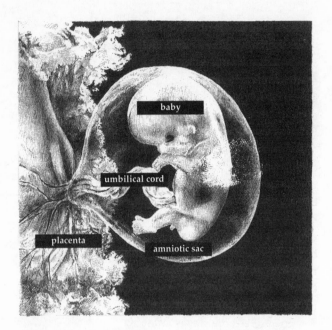

Inside the womb, the baby floats in a bag of fluid called the AMNIOTIC SAC. This is like a cushion surrounding and protecting the baby. The baby has no need to breathe air through its nose and mouth because it gets oxygen from its mother through the placenta.

The UMBILICAL CORD is the baby's lifeline. It joins the baby to the placenta. Three blood vessels run along it, twisted together. One carries oxygen and food to the baby, two carry waste matter away.

The PLACENTA is rooted to the lining of the womb. It acts as a link between the mother's blood supply and the baby's. Food, oxygen and antibodies (which protect the baby against infection) pass from the mother's bloodstream across the placenta and are carried to the baby along the umbilical cord. Waste matter from the baby's bloodstream passes back along the same route to be got rid of through the mother's system.

BIRTH

When a baby is born, the muscles of the womb push the baby down the vagina and out through the opening between the mother's legs. The vagina and vaginal opening are very elastic and stretch to let the baby pass through.

Giving birth to a baby is hard work, which is why it is called **LABOUR**. It is uncomfortable, and it can be painful. It is more painful for some women than for others, not just because every woman's experience of labour and birth is different but also because pain is very individual in any case. Most women feel that this is a worthwhile pain because they have their baby at the end of it. There are a number of ways in which the pain can be lessened. For example, breathing and relaxing in particular ways can help, or some women choose to use pain-relieving drugs.

There are three stages to labour.

In the **FIRST STAGE OF LABOUR**, the cervix (the neck of the womb) gradually opens until it is wide enough for the baby's head to pass through. The muscles of the womb contract and this pulls the cervix up and opens it out. The cervix is said to be 'dilating' which simply means 'opening up'.

This part of labour can take quite a long time – usually about six to twelve hours. The mother relaxes as much as she can and usually tries to keep on the move. As the contractions of the womb muscles get stronger they hurt more, but breathing deeply and rhythmically usually helps a mother cope with the contractions. She will also have a midwife, and probably her partner or a friend, to support and help her.

The **SECOND STAGE OF LABOUR** begins when the

105

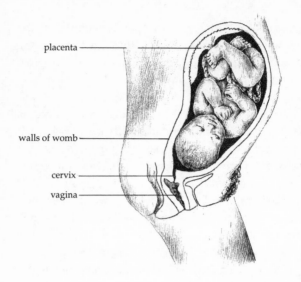

placenta

walls of womb

cervix

vagina

cervix is wide enough to let the baby through (that is, fully dilated) and the mother begins to feel that she wants to push the baby out. The muscles of the womb begin to contract in a different way, pushing the baby down the vagina. The womb muscles do most of the work, but the mother can help by pushing down with the muscles in her abdomen. The baby's head appears first through the vaginal opening and the body quickly follows. A midwife or doctor helps to deliver the baby. The second stage is much quicker than the first, usually no more than an hour for women having their first babies and often much less.

The baby starts to breathe as soon as his or her head is born, so the umbilical cord is no longer needed. Soon

106

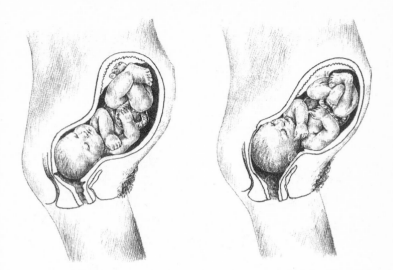

During the first stage of labour, the cervix gradually opens up until it is wide enough for the baby's head to pass through.

after delivery, the cord is cut, close to where it joins the baby, leaving a little stump attached to the baby's navel. Before it is cut, a plastic clamp is put on the cord to stop it bleeding. There are no nerves in the cord, so cutting it doesn't hurt either the baby or the mother. After a few days, the stump dries and drops off, leaving the baby with a normal navel or 'belly button'.

In the THIRD STAGE OF LABOUR, the muscles of the womb contract again to push out the placenta, which also passes down the vagina and out between the woman's legs. Like the umbilical cord, the placenta is no longer needed. When the placenta comes out, it looks rather like a large piece of red-blue liver, about the size of a dinner plate.

107

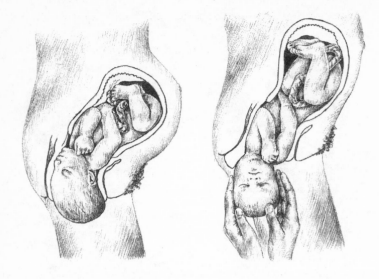

In the second stage of labour, the baby is pushed down the vagina and out of the vaginal opening.

CAESAREAN DELIVERIES

Sometimes it isn't safe for a baby to be born through the vagina. For example, if either the mother or baby is unwell, the baby will need to be delivered quickly. The mother may then have a Caesarean section. She is given an anaesthetic so she won't feel anything, and a small cut is made low down on her abdomen and then through the wall of the womb. The baby can then be lifted out.

 WHEN PREGNANCY GOES WRONG

Sadly, not all pregnancies end with the birth of a healthy baby. Sometimes a baby dies quite early in the pregnancy. If this happens before 24 weeks, it is called a **miscarriage**. A lot of women lose a baby like this: it is estimated that as many as one in five pregnancies end in miscarriage.

Sometimes a baby dies later in pregnancy, or during birth, or soon after he or she is born. A baby who is already dead when he or she is born is said to be **stillborn**. In the UK, at least one in every 100 babies is either stillborn or dies within the first four weeks of life.

Sometimes tests carried out in pregnancy show that a baby is not developing normally or has a condition which means it couldn't survive. The parents then have to make the very difficult decision whether or not to carry on with the pregnancy. If they decide not to carry on, the pregnancy is brought to an end. This is called **termination for abnormality**. Terminations (or abortions) may also be carried out for other reasons – for example, because it would damage the mother's health to continue the pregnancy, or because the mother couldn't cope with having the baby. The law lays down clear rules about when, and for what reasons, a pregnancy can be terminated.

Many people hold strong views on abortion. Some believe that it is wrong because they feel the unborn child, however abnormal, has a right to live. Others believe that women should have the right to choose whether or not to have the baby.

In medical language, the word 'abortion' or 'spontaneous abortion' is also used to refer to a miscarriage.   **109**

CONTRACEPTION AND FAMILY PLANNING

TALKING ABOUT CONTRACEPTION

◆ Children can't understand either the need for contraception or the mechanics of it unless they know exactly what happens during sexual intercourse and how a baby is conceived. So it's important to make sure that they are clear about these things first (see Sexual Intercourse, pages 83 to 85, and Conception, pages 95 to 99).

――――

◆ Try to explain why contraception is needed. You can talk about the different reasons that people may have for wanting to avoid pregnancy:
  ● medical reasons.
  ● financial reasons.
  ● not feeling ready to take on the responsibility of bringing up a child.
  ● being too young to have a baby.
  ● wanting to plan when they have children and how many to have.

Thinking and talking about these reasons can help children see that using contraception is responsible and caring.

――――

◆ By giving children the facts about contraception, it's important not to seem to be putting pressure on them to have sex. Talking about contraception is important, but so too is talking about choosing whether or not to have sex. (See pages 153 to 157.)

110

◆   Some parents hold beliefs which mean they do
     not want their children to be sexually active or use
     contraception. But when teenagers do become
     sexually active, it is vital that they understand that
     some contraceptives, as well as preventing an
     unwanted pregnancy, give some protection
     against sexually transmitted diseases, including
     HIV. See page 127 for more information.

CONTRACEPTION: WHAT CHILDREN NEED TO KNOW

─────────── **INFORMATION TO MAKE CHOICES** ───────────

Younger children (who haven't yet reached puberty)
need to learn what contraception is and that there are
different ways of avoiding pregnancy. Older children
and teenagers need detailed, comprehensive information about methods of contraception so that they can
assess and compare the different options that are available. This should include information about what protection the different methods give against sexually
transmitted diseases.

   Children need to know about the kinds of contraceptives available, and where to get them, *before* the
time when they may choose to become sexually active.
They should also know that a girl becomes fertile (able
to have a baby) from the time of her first period, which
could be when she's as young as nine or ten. A boy
becomes fertile from the time he first ejaculates, which
could be as early as 12 years old.

   It's important for children to understand that they   **111** can choose not to have sexual intercourse. This may mean resisting a lot of pressure, both from friends and from the media. But if they do choose to have sex, and don't want a baby, then it's essential that they know they need to use contraception.

Sometimes children need someone other than their parents to talk to about whether or not to have sexual intercourse. It helps if you can recognize this and perhaps even discuss who would be a good person for your child to talk to.

☐ CONTRACEPTION AS A SHARED RESPONSIBILITY ☐

It's important for children to understand that contraception is ideally a joint responsibility shared by both sexual partners, no matter what method is used. It's all too easy to see the condom as a man's responsibility and other forms of contraception (IUD, pill etc.) as a woman's responsibility. But both partners can jointly decide what form of contraception is best for them; and both can take responsibility for making sure that it *is* used correctly every time. You can also explain that different methods suit different couples at different times of their lives.

CONTRACEPTION: THE FACTS

☐ WHO NEEDS CONTRACEPTION? ☐

Many children and teenagers still have mistaken ideas about when and how you can or can't get pregnant. The facts are that a girl *can* get pregnant:

- the first time she has intercourse.
- even if she has a hot bath afterwards.

112

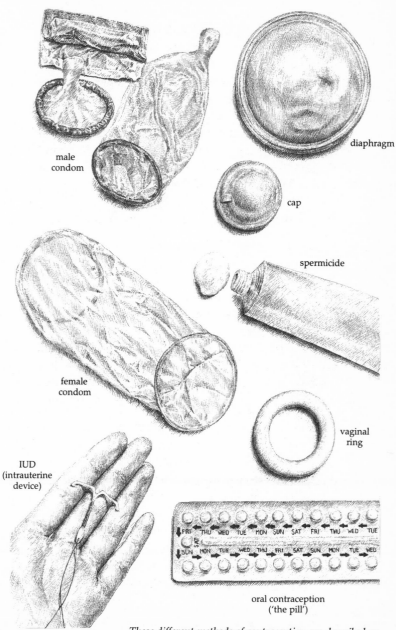

diaphragm

male
condom

cap

spermicide

female
condom

vaginal
ring

IUD
(intrauterine
device)

oral contraception
('the pill')

These different methods of contraception are described on
pages 114 to 121.

- even if the boy or man pulls his penis out of her vagina before he ejaculates.
- even if she doesn't 'come' or have an orgasm.
- even if she has intercourse during a period.
- whatever position she uses.
- even if semen just gets *near* the vagina, without the penis being put inside the vagina at all.

METHODS OF CONTRACEPTION

Contraception effectiveness

If a method of contraception is said to be 85 per cent effective it means that out of 100 women using the method for one year, 85 would not be pregnant at the end of the year.

▭ THE MALE CONDOM ▭

Also called: the sheath, protective, rubber, Johnny.

- **How does it work?** The condom is a thin rubber sheath which is pulled over the erect penis well before there is any contact between penis and vagina. When the man ejaculates, the semen is caught in the end of the condom. Each condom should be used only once. See pages 116 to 117 for illustrations showing how to use a male condom.
- **How effective is it?** The condom is between 85 per cent and 98 per cent effective if it is good quality (the packet should carry a Kitemark) and if it is used correctly. The condom is more effective if it is used with a spermicide – a cream or jelly containing a chemical which kills sperm. Some condoms have a built-in spermicide.

- **Advantages and disadvantages** Condoms are easy to get hold of (see page 124) and easy to use. They help protect both partners against sexually transmitted diseases, including HIV (see Safer Sex, page 137) and give women some protection against cervical cancer.

  Some women find condoms a bit dry so it helps to use a water-based lubricant such as KY jelly. Lotions or creams containing oil or fat of any kind should never be used with a condom because they damage the rubber. If a condom is not put on properly, it might slip off during intercourse. There's also a slight risk of the condom splitting.

- **Putting on a condom** It's essential to put a condom on correctly (see pages 116 to 117). This can take a bit of practice. People who feel confident about putting a condom on are much more likely to use one. Women as well as men should know how it's done. Some couples make putting on a condom a part of their lovemaking.

  Take care not to tear or puncture the condom when getting it out of the packet or at any other time. Sharp nails or rings, for example, can snag the rubber.

THE FEMALE CONDOM

The female condom is now becoming available.

- **How does it work?** A female condom is a sheath made of soft polyurethane. It is about 18 cm (7 in) long, with a ring about 7.5 cm (3 in) in diameter at the open end and another smaller ring inside the condom at its closed end. A woman puts the

PUTTING ON A CONDOM

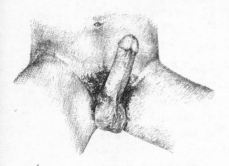

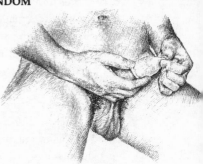

Wait until the penis is erect.

Hold the condom by the closed end, squeezing the tip shut between the thumb and forefinger to squeeze out any bubble of air and make a space for the semen.

Slip the open end of the condom over the end of the penis and unroll the condom down the shaft.

closed end into her vagina, leaving the larger ring outside. It lines the vagina and the area just outside the vagina and stops the sperm from reaching the ovum. Each condom should be used only once.

- **How effective is it?** This is a new contraceptive and there is no information available yet about effectiveness. But it is expected to be as reliable as the male condom.
- **Advantages and disadvantages** It is easy to get and use. It helps to protect both partners against sexually transmitted diseases, including HIV. It may also help to protect women against cervical cancer.

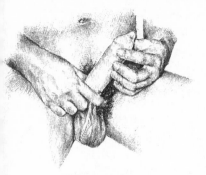

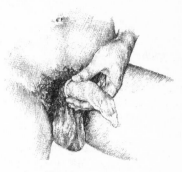

Hold onto the open end of the condom as the penis enters the vagina, to make sure the condom doesn't slip off. Hold the condom in the same way when pulling the penis out of the vagina, either during lovemaking or after ejaculating.

After ejaculating, the man slips out of the woman while his penis is still erect, holding the open end of the condom. The semen will be caught in the tip of the condom. As his penis softens, he can pull the condom off, taking care not to spill any semen, wrap it in loo paper and flush it away.

THE DIAPHRAGM OR CAP WITH SPERMICIDE

- **How do they work?** The diaphragm is a soft dome of rubber that fits right across the cervix. The cap is smaller and just fits over the end of the cervix. Both prevent sperm reaching the ovum. They always have to be used with a spermicide. The woman puts the diaphragm or cap into her vagina before having intercourse. It has to be left in place for at least six hours afterwards, then taken out.

- **How effective are they?** If used correctly, they are 98 per cent effective.

- **Advantages and disadvantages** The diaphragm or cap can be put in before lovemaking begins, so

117

there's no interruption to lovemaking. (If a diaphragm or cap is put in more than three hours before intercourse, some more spermicide is needed when lovemaking begins.) Both the diaphragm and cap give some protection against cervical cancer, but not against all sexually transmitted diseases.

The diaphragm and cap have to be supplied by a doctor or family planning clinic to make sure they fit and they have to be checked every six months to make sure they are still the right size.

THE IUD (INTRAUTERINE DEVICE)

Also called: IUCD (intrauterine contraceptive device), coil, loop.

- **How does it work?** The IUD is a small plastic or plastic and copper Y-shaped object which is put into a woman's womb and left there. It stops the ovum and the sperm meeting, or prevents the fertilized ovum implanting in the womb lining.

- **How effective is it?** The IUD is 97 to 99 per cent effective.

- **Advantages and disadvantages** The IUD has to be put in by a doctor but once in place it can be forgotten about and it is very effective. It is particularly suitable for women who have already had children. However, there are some types which can be used by women who have not. It can also be used as emergency contraception (see page 123).

The IUD can sometimes make periods heavier. Another problem is that it can come out. In addition there is a risk of infection. The IUD is not the best contraceptive for young women who have never been pregnant as it may be more difficult to put in.

THE VAGINAL RING

This contraceptive is just becoming available.

- **How does it work?** This is a soft rubber ring which is put into the vagina and left there. It is taken out every three months and changed for a new one. The ring releases a progestogen hormone which causes changes in the mucus in the cervix. These changes make it difficult for sperm to get into the womb to meet an ovum. In some women, the vaginal ring stops the ovaries producing ova each month.

- **How effective is it?** The vaginal ring is 95 to 96 per cent effective.

- **Advantages and disadvantages** The vaginal ring doesn't interrupt lovemaking because it is in the vagina all the time, but it does have to be fitted by a doctor. It can cause periods to become irregular and sometimes there is bleeding between periods. A few women get vaginal irritation or discharge and, very occasionally, a vaginal ring comes out.

THE PROGESTOGEN-ONLY PILL

Also called: the mini-pill.

- **How does it work?** The pill contains an artificial progestogen hormone which affects the mucus in the cervix, making it thicker and hostile to sperm. **119**

It also makes the womb lining unsuitable for the implantation of a fertilized ovum and sometimes it stops ovulation.

- **How effective is it?** If taken every day at the same time, it is 98 per cent effective.
- **Advantages and disadvantages** The pill is easy to take and doesn't have to be taken at the time of having intercourse. But it has to be taken at the same time every day and can be unreliable if it is taken two or more hours late. It is thought not to have the health risks of the combined pill (see below) but it can cause irregular, unpredictable bleeding. Sickness or diarrhoea can stop it working.

THE COMBINED PILL

- **How does it work?** The pill contains artificial oestrogen and progestogen hormones which stop ovulation.
- **How effective is it?** Almost 100 per cent effective, if taken correctly.
- **Advantages and disadvantages** The combined pill is easy to take and a very reliable contraceptive, although it is less reliable if it is taken more than 12 hours late, or if pills are missed, or if you have sickness or diarrhoea or are taking certain drugs or antibiotics. The pill gives a woman an absolutely regular monthly cycle with lighter, less painful bleeding and often reduced PMS (premenstrual syndrome). But some women get side effects such as weight gain, nausea or loss of libido (the desire to have sex).

There is still uncertainty about the long-term risks of taking the combined pill. It is known that it can increase the risk of thrombosis (blood-clotting) for women over 35 who smoke, or are overweight, or have high blood pressure. There is also some evidence that taking the combined pill over a long period of time may slightly increase the risk of breast and possibly cervical cancer in some women.

WITHDRAWAL

- **How does it work?** The man withdraws or takes his penis out of the woman's vagina just before he reaches his orgasm and ejaculates.
- **How effective is it?** Withdrawal is not very effective. It is probably about 50 per cent effective, but a lot depends on how it is done.
- **Advantages and disadvantages** The one advantage of withdrawal is that it doesn't involve any kind of planning by either partner. The greatest disadvantage is that it isn't very effective. It demands a lot of self-control on the man's part, and a great deal of trust on the woman's. The man has to judge the right moment to withdraw but, in fact, even if he judges the moment to perfection and withdraws just before ejaculation, there is still a good chance that some semen will already have leaked out of the penis and into the vagina. Even a drop of semen can contain millions of sperm.

NATURAL METHODS

- **How do they work?** If a woman can find out when she is likely to ovulate, she can avoid

121

having intercourse around that time. There are a number of ways of finding out when ovulation takes place. She can use a calendar (ovulation usually takes place 14 days before a period); she can take her temperature every day (the body temperature usually rises at the time of ovulation); and she can note changes in vaginal wetness (wetness usually increases around the time of ovulation). All these things have to be done correctly and records have to be kept over some months before ovulation can be predicted.

- **How effective are they?** Natural methods of contraception can be up to 98 per cent effective if all the methods are used in combination and are used carefully. When natural methods are not carefully or correctly used, they are far less effective.

- **Advantages and disadvantages** These methods are 'natural' in the sense that they don't involve any mechanical devices or hormones. This means there are no possible side effects. But avoiding intercourse for the many days when a woman is likely to be fertile demands control and commitment from both partners.

WHERE TO GO FOR CONTRACEPTION

Information and advice on contraception are available free from:

- **GPs (family doctors).** You can go to your own GP or a different one. Lists of GPs are kept in libraries, post offices and advice centres, and GPs who offer advice on contraception have the letter 'C' after their name.

EMERGENCY CONTRACEPTION

If for any reason a girl or woman has sex without contraception being used, or if a couple have used contraception but have made a mistake with the result that it won't work, it is still possible to prevent an unwanted pregnancy. It's important to act quickly – the sooner the better. Up to three days after having intercourse, the woman can take two special doses of the combined pill. Up to five days after having intercourse, the woman can have an IUD inserted.

These methods are for emergencies only. The emergency pill is 96 to 99 per cent effective. The IUD is almost 100 per cent effective.

- **Family Planning clinics.** Look in your phone book under 'family planning' to find the address of your nearest clinic, or phone the Family Planning Association (see page 162). Some family planning clinics run special sessions for young people.
- **Brook Advisory Centres, or** other centres which are run especially for young people. To find your nearest Brook Centre, look in your phone book or phone the Brook main office (details on page 162). Your health authority (number in your phone book under your health authority's name) should be able to tell you of any other advisory centres for young people.

Condoms are available free from some family planning clinics and GPs, and from Brook Advisory Centres. You can buy condoms and spermicides from chemists or pharmacies, supermarkets, barbers, garages and other shops as well as from slot machines and by mail order.

All other kinds of contraception (the pill, IUD etc.) are available free from family planning clinics, Brook Advisory Centres and GPs.

All contraceptive services are confidential, including for under 16 year olds. But a doctor is likely to encourage anyone under 16 to talk to and involve their parents if at all possible.

SEXUALLY TRANSMITTED DISEASES (STDs)

TALKING ABOUT STDs

◆ Before children can learn about sexually transmitted diseases, including HIV and AIDS, they need a good grasp of what happens during sexual intercourse, and also some understanding of sexual behaviour. In order to be able to understand how STDs spread, they need to know that people may have sex with more than one partner.

◆ It's important to avoid giving the impression that STDs are 'dirty' and only caught by people who are promiscuous, or whose sexual behaviour is in some way unusual or immoral. If children come to see STDs as embarrassing, or even as evidence of some kind of sexual misbehaviour, then they may not feel able to get treatment if they themselves become infected later on, however that may happen.

It's also important not to be alarmist. With HIV and AIDS so much in the news, it can be hard to remember that there are a large number of different STDs, many of which are common diseases that can be treated and cured.

◆ Talking about STDs (and unwanted pregnancy) means talking about risk, and risk is a difficult idea for children to grasp. Because their

125

experience is limited, they find it hard to look ahead and see what the consequences of certain actions might be. At first, it's easier for children to understand about risk if you can give examples that are closer to their own experience, for example the risk of falling off a bike because of riding too fast. Understanding the risk involved in sex will follow later.

◆ Most teenagers at some time or another face a decision about 'how far to go' in a relationship, and for some this is (or becomes) a decision about whether or not to have sex. They need to be able to talk this over with their partner and, if they do decide to have sex together, they need to know how to protect themselves by using a condom. This can take courage and confidence, and it is a great deal easier if they are well-informed and don't feel embarrassed talking about sex.

◆ Information about STDs and safer sex go together. Although safer sex is a practical health matter and it may help children to see it that way, it's also important to talk about the issues involved – what it means for a relationship, what kind of responsibility is entailed (towards oneself and others), how it can be talked about with a partner, and so on.

◆ Talking about STDs and safer sex can seem very anti-sex. For parents of teenagers, it can be
126 especially difficult to be positive about sex but also

realistic about risk, and to encourage responsibility without being heavy-handed. The information in Talking About Sex, pages 77 to 78, may help.

STDs: WHAT CHILDREN NEED TO KNOW

REDUCING THE RISK OF STDs

Children need to know what sexually transmitted diseases are, how they are passed from one person to another, how they can be treated and, above all, how people can protect themselves against getting them. Information about safer sex is vital and children need this information well before they might choose to become sexually active, so that they can protect themselves not only against STDs but also against unwanted pregnancy.

Older children are likely to be aware of the importance of safer sex, but they may not know very much about how to practise it. Practical details, including where to get condoms and how to put them on (see page 116), are very important.

Children also need to be clear about the difference between the risk of becoming pregnant and the risk of catching an STD. Pregnancy can be avoided by using contraception, but not all contraceptives protect against STDs. For example, if a boy has a girlfriend who is on the pill, then he doesn't need to use a condom in order to protect her against becoming pregnant, but he *does* need to use a condom to protect both himself and her against STDs.

127

HIV AND AIDS

There is so much about HIV and AIDS in the media that children cannot help but hear about them. Even so, it's surprisingly difficult for children to get accurate information, and there are a lot of myths around about how HIV is passed on, who gets AIDS, and so on. It's important that children know the facts, and that they can also distinguish between fact, opinion and attitude.

The most important fact of all is that using a male condom correctly gives the maximum protection possible against all sexually transmitted diseases, including HIV.

STDs: THE FACTS

There are many different sexually transmitted diseases, some more serious than others. They are all diseases, or infections, that are passed from one person to another by sexual contact. Some infections, like cystitis and thrush, can be caught in other ways too.

Other words that are used for STDs are sexually transmitted infections (STIs), veneral disease (VD), or genito-urinary infections.

Anybody who is having sex can get a sexually transmitted disease, whether they are heterosexual or homosexual. But practising safer sex (see pages 137 to 138) protects against STDS.

Most STDs can affect both men and women. They usually affect the genitals, or the bladder and urethra, and sometimes they can affect other parts of the body.

Some STDs have very clear symptoms but others have

no symptoms, or not to start with, so people may not know they have them. Symptoms can be:

- an unusual discharge from the vagina or penis.
- blisters, warts or spots near the vagina, penis or anus.
- a rash, irritation or soreness around the vagina, penis or anus.
- pain, discomfort or a burning feeling when passing urine.
- passing urine more often than usual.

Most STDs can be treated and cured. Some can lead to more serious conditions if they aren't treated. For example, untreated gonorrhea in women can lead to pelvic inflammatory disease which can make it difficult for a woman to get pregnant and may even make it impossible for her to have children at all. (But of course not all infertility is due to infection. There are many other causes.)

These are just some of the many different STDs:

CHLAMYDIA affects the genitals and sometimes the eyes and throat. It's passed from one person to another by vaginal, anal or oral sex. Often there are no symptoms, but women may get a vaginal discharge and pain when passing urine. Men may also have pain when passing urine, or may lose a little white fluid from the penis. Chlamydia can be treated with antibiotics.

CYSTITIS is an inflammation of the bladder caused by bacteria that normally live in the rectum and around

129

the anus. During sexual intercourse, the bacteria can be transferred to the urethra and so on to the bladder. Sexual intercourse itself can also trigger cystitis. But the cause is often non-sexual. See page 133.

GENITAL HERPES is a virus that can be passed from one person to another through vaginal, anal or oral sex. Symptoms are itching, tingling or aching in the vulva, penis or testes. Sores then appear around the genitals. Passing urine can become painful, and some people get flu-like symptoms. The sores change into blisters that usually burst and heal themselves. There's no cure for genital herpes but there are various ways of easing the discomfort.

A different type of herpes virus causes cold sores on the lips, face and mouth. These sores are not sexually transmitted but can cause genital herpes through oral sex.

GENITAL WARTS are small growths on the genitals and sometimes around and inside the anus. When they're small they feel like little bumps of skin, but they can grow into quite large, cauliflower-like lumps. They are caused by a virus and are passed from one person to another by skin contact. So they can be passed on by having sex with someone who's infected. The warts can be difficult to get rid of: usually they are removed by painting on a special liquid. It's important to get genital warts treated because there is a possible link with cervical cancer.

GONORRHEA is an infection which can affect the vagina, cervix, urethra, rectum or even the throat. It's passed from one person to another by vaginal, anal or oral sex. Often there are no symptoms, so people may not know that they've got it unless they have a test. Some women notice an unusual change in their vaginal discharge, pain when passing urine, or a sore throat. Men may have a discharge from the penis, pain when passing urine, itching or discharge from the anus, or a sore throat. Gonorrhea can be treated with antibiotics.

NON-SPECIFIC URETHRITIS (NSU) is an inflammation of the urethra (in men), and an inflammation of the urethra or, more usually, of the cervix (in women). It can be caused by several different bacteria, which is why it is called non-specific. The most common bacterium to cause NSU is chlamydia (see page 135). It's passed from one person to another by vaginal, anal or oral sex. Sometimes NSU causes a burning feeling when passing urine, and men may lose a little white, cloudy fluid from the penis. But often there are no symptoms and people can have NSU and pass it on to their partner without knowing they have it. NSU can be treated with antibiotics.

PUBIC LICE are tiny lice that live in pubic hair and can be spread by close physical contact with someone who has them. They make the genitals very itchy. Treatment is with a special lotion which kills the lice. Ordinary washing doesn't get rid of them.

THRUSH (CANDIDIASIS) is a fungal infection that can be passed on by having vaginal, anal or oral sex. It's also possible to get thrush in non-sexual ways. See the opposite page for more information.

TV (TRICHOMONIASIS) is an infection caused by a tiny parasite sometimes found in the vagina and urethra. It's passed on by having sex with someone who's infected. Symptoms for women are a thin yellow or green vaginal discharge, which may be frothy and smell unpleasant, and a sore, itchy vagina. Men may have no symptoms and may not know they've got it. TV can be treated with appropriate medication.

 **GETTING TREATMENT FOR STDs**

Treatment for STDs is available from GPs and from Special Clinics – clinics which specialize in the treatment of STDs. GPs may treat an STD themselves or refer a patient to a Special Clinic. Special Clinics are also called STD clinics, GUM (genito-urinary medicine) clinics, or even VD (venereal disease) clinics, although this is an old name that isn't used very much any more.

Anyone who thinks they may have an STD, or who knows they have been at risk of catching one, no matter what their age and even if they have no symptoms, can go direct to a Special Clinic for help, advice and treatment. There's no need for a referral or doctor's letter. Treatment is free and absolutely confidential.

Addresses and phone numbers of Special Clinics are usually listed in telephone directories under the name of the local health authority. They may be listed as genito-urinary clinics, STD clinics or VD clinics.

Special Clinics are usually attached to a main hospital and can also be contacted through the hospital. The Family Planning Association (see page 162) runs a Clinics Enquiries Service, and Brook Advisory Centres also run a helpline (see page 162).

CYSTITIS AND THRUSH

Both cystitis and thrush are common infections that can be caused by sex but more often have other causes.

CYSTITIS is more common in women than men. It can be caused by bacteria from the bowel, rectum and anus entering the urethra and bladder. Sometimes the bacteria get into the urethra during sexual intercourse, but it can happen in other ways too. This is why it is important that girls and women always wipe themselves from front to back after going to the loo. Cystitis can also be an allergic reaction to perfumed soap, or a vaginal deodorant, and it can be caused by other infections, such as thrush (see page 131–2). Symptoms may be a burning feeling when passing urine, the need to pass urine more often (though often there's little to pass), the feeling of *wanting* to pass urine all the time, an ache low down in the abdomen or back, cloudy urine or blood in the urine, and feverishness.

It's sometimes possible to treat cystitis at home, without going to the doctor. There are five things that you can do to help:

- drink a lot of water – a pint at the first signs of infection, then half a pint or more every 20 minutes. This helps to flush the bacteria out of the bladder.

133

- go to the loo very often to empty the bladder.
- take a teaspoon of bicarbonate of soda mixed in water, every hour for three hours. This makes the urine less acidic, so it relieves the burning feeling and stops the bacteria multiplying.
- take a mild painkiller.
- hold a hot water bottle between the thighs or against the back.

After three hours of this treatment, the cystitis usually begins to calm down. Anyone who has repeated attacks of cystitis, has blood in their urine, or is pregnant, should see their doctor.

THRUSH is an infection caused by a yeast called *Candida albicans*. Everyone has this yeast in their body and normally it causes no harm. But sometimes it multiplies and gets out of control and then it causes infections, especially in women. The symptoms are itching around the vulva and a thick white discharge from the vagina; or, in men, a sore, itchy penis. Thrush can be passed on by having vaginal, anal or oral sex, but it's also possible to get it in non-sexual ways. For example, many women get thrush when they are pregnant. And sometimes antibiotics, or vaginal deodorants, or perfumed soap can trigger the infection by upsetting the usual balance of bacteria in the vagina.

A doctor can prescribe medication which usually clears thrush up quite quickly. For women, this can be given as pessaries, which are inserted into the vagina like a tampon. It's best not to have baths or wash frequently to ease the itching because although a bath is soothing at first, it makes the irritation worse in the end. Wash with plain water only, no soap, and no disinfectant. Some women also find it soothing to put some plain, live yoghurt around the vulva and/or in the vagina. The bacteria in the yoghurt help restore the usual balance of bacteria in the vagina. To get the yoghurt into the vagina, dip a tampon in yoghurt and insert it.

PREGNANCY AND STDs

Women who have an STD and are pregnant may pass the infection on to their baby. So it's especially important that any STDs are treated during pregnancy. Sometimes a baby can catch an STD from its mother during delivery. Doctors need to know in advance if there is a risk of this happening so that they can protect the baby from infection.

HIV AND AIDS

HIV stands for human immunodeficiency virus. It is a virus that can damage the body's immune system – the body's system for fighting illness.

An important part of the body's immune system are the white blood cells which fight off and kill infections. When someone becomes infected with HIV, the HIV lives inside their body in one particular kind of white blood cell called the T-helper cell. The HIV may, in time, kill the T-helper cells and this weakens the immune system so much that the body can no longer fight off infections. The person may then become seriously ill with a number of different infections or diseases. AIDS

135

is the name for this collection of illnesses. AIDS stands for acquired immune deficiency syndrome.

It is very important to understand that it's possible to be infected by HIV but not to have AIDS – in other words, to be carrying the virus but not to have the disease. People with HIV can be quite healthy and can lead a normal life for many years. No one can see they have HIV, but they could still infect others. Experts think that most people who are HIV-infected do eventually get HIV-related symptoms or AIDS. At present there is no known cure for AIDS, although help can be given to control the secondary infections.

HIV is found in body fluids such as blood, semen and vaginal fluid. It can be passed from one person to another if the body fluids of someone who is infected get into someone else's body. This can happen:

- by having unprotected vaginal or anal intercourse with someone who is infected with HIV.
  (Unprotected means without using a condom.)
- by sharing needles and other equipment for injecting drugs with someone who is infected with HIV.
- by an HIV-infected mother passing the infection on to her baby, either during pregnancy or during delivery.

In the past some people have caught HIV because they have been given a blood transfusion of infected blood. In the UK all blood is now checked for HIV before it is used.

In the UK at present, the only way anyone can know whether or not they have HIV is by having a blood test – the HIV antibody test. This is why safer sex is so important to protect against possible infection (see opposite).

MYTHS ABOUT HIV

You *can't* catch HIV:

- by hugging, kissing or being close to some-one who has HIV.
- by wearing their clothes.
- by sharing a cup, glass or cutlery, or sharing food.
- by sharing towels.
- from mosquitoes or other blood-sucking insects.
- from a toilet seat.
- from showers, baths or swimming-pools.
- by sharing a toothbrush or razor.
- from tears, sweat or saliva.

SAFER SEX

Safer sex is having sex in a way that cuts down, or cuts out, the risk of catching a sexually transmitted disease, including HIV. This means:

- always using a condom for vaginal or anal intercourse. Both the male and female condom (see pages 114 and 115) help protect against STDs, including HIV. The risk of becoming infected with HIV by having oral sex is thought to be very small, but other STDs, such as gonorrhoea and herpes, can be passed on in this

137

way, so some people prefer to use a condom for oral sex as well.

OR

- having sex without the penis entering either the vagina or anus. For example, some couples enjoy touching each other (masturbating).

To practise safer sex and enjoy it both partners need to be able to talk and decide together in what ways they want to make love. This needn't include penetrative sex. It's vital that neither partner depends on the other to take the sole responsibility for safer sex: both partners should be equally responsible.

THINKING IT THROUGH

Talking about sex can raise many different issues on which people hold different and often strong opinions. Children need to be aware of these issues, to know that people's views and values differ and, eventually, to be able to think things through for themselves. This part of the book looks at:

- **Sex in the media** (p 140)
- **Sexism** (p 145)
- **Learning about sexuality** (p 147)
- **Pressures and choices** (p 153)
- **The risk of abuse** (p 157)
- **Telling it as it is** (p 160)

SEX IN THE MEDIA

The media can be a valuable source of information about sex. Some teenage and women's magazines, for example, run articles on subjects like cervical smears, testicular cancer, under-age sex, children and AIDS, that are factual, up-to-date and helpful. Television programmes, including programmes on children's television, deal with similar, sensitive issues. But at the other extreme, sex is sensationalized by the media. Newspaper headlines ('Vicar caught in three-in-a-bed sex scandal') that are amusing, or titillating, for adults, can be very perplexing for children.

As adults, we're used to the way that sex is portrayed in the media and may not even notice it very much. We may not particularly *like* the amount of sex that is shown on television, or the way women are pictured in the newspapers, or the way sex is used to advertise anything from cars to chocolates to vacuum cleaners, but we accept it, more or less, as yet another fact of life. Sometimes, of course, we enjoy it – which is partly why it is there in the first place. But seen through a child's, or even a teenager's eyes, the daily diet of sex in the media is, at best, puzzling, and at worst, disturbing.

We get a lot of wrong ideas. TV makes it seem like sex is just like kissing. They make it out to be so easy, and it's really not that easy.
(13-YEAR-OLD GIRL.)

When I see films about people having sex, I don't understand them, because they don't look at all like real life. Why is the woman always scared – scared of having

sex? And why does the man hate her? I don't like it when the man hates her.
(10-YEAR-OLD BOY.)

On the television, you always see the man in control of any sexual relationship. And they don't ever show any responsibility in their sexual relationships. There's never any sign of condoms or any other contraceptives.
(16-YEAR-OLD GIRL.)

I think the telly's really confusing, because they show people having sex and making love and everything, but they don't show the relationship, or how anyone feels. They just show that you have sex, and then it's all done with. I don't think they should do that, because it's not only having sex, it's having a relationship, and working things out with your partner.
(12-YEAR-OLD GIRL.)

I don't think I want to do it, the way you see it on TV. People say it's dirty.
(11-YEAR-OLD BOY.)

In the media, sex appears in lots of different guises and very few of them are realistic. Often it's made out to be glamorous. It involves beautiful people with perfect bodies. Or it is sordid, and sometimes violent. It's almost always irresponsible, with no mention of contraception and no discussion of risk. No one stops, at the critical moment, to put on a condom.

It isn't just sexual intercourse and sexual behaviour that are treated unrealistically in the media. Pregnancy and birth, for example, are made either much *less*, or much *more* dramatic than in real life. Relationships are played at double speed: they develop, become sexual and are over within weeks or even days. Even factual programmes can sometimes be misleading for children.

> *I was watching television one afternoon with my youngest son and there was a programme about childbirth and they showed a Caesarean. And he said, 'Is that where babies come from?' I said, 'No', and I tried to explain that sometimes, if there's a problem, babies come from the tummy, but that there are also other places that babies come from . . .*

The reason that sex in the media can be so confusing for children is that to understand what is happening or what is being said, you need knowledge and experience that children simply haven't got. Their lack of knowledge and experience doesn't make them unaware of sexual messages, but it makes those messages hard for them to interpret.

Children need to be protected from inappropriate films, videos, television programmes, newspaper articles, and so on. Some parents put more emphasis on protecting their children than others, and different people make different judgements about what is inappropriate, but most would agree that there are *some* things children should not see, and *some* information that children should not have. Most parents would also agree that no matter how hard you try, it is impossible to protect your child from *all* inappropriate information. Even if you make sure that your child doesn't watch a particular late-night programme, there's a good chance that another child at school will watch it, and will tell everyone else all about it.

So children need information to counterbalance and make sense of what they see and hear. They need to be able to sort out what is myth and what is reality, and understand a bit about why the myths are created.

> *My nine-year-old came downstairs one night because she couldn't sleep. We were watching a serial on the television and she curled up on the sofa with me and we went on watching. There was quite a lurid sex scene, with a lot of panting and rolling about and a very obvious moment of climax. So afterwards, although she didn't ask about it, I tried to talk about what the couple were doing, and why they were making a noise. And because I thought she might think that my partner and I made love like that, I said something about the way it was made to look, so people would enjoy watching it, and the different ways people enjoy loving each other. She accepted all that and it was fine. But I think she'd have been very puzzled if I hadn't said anything.*

If you are aware of what your children are seeing in the media, you can supply some of the information and explanation they need. Explaining the newspaper headlines may not be easy but it's worth having a try. ('They've found out that a vicar has been having sex with his wife and someone else at the same time. A lot of people think that's wrong, and they think vicars, even more than other people, shouldn't do anything wrong.') Gradually, you can help your child to think more critically about why the media portray and use sex in the way that they do. If you look together at news-papers and magazines or at television commercials, you can see how frequently sex is used to sell things. (For example, newspapers with stories about sexy vicars sell more copies.) You can talk about why this is done, and (with older children) whether it is acceptable.

The box below lists some of the things that you could talk about. You can tackle some of these issues with 10-, 11- and 12-year-olds as well as with teenagers.

TALKING ABOUT SEX IN THE MEDIA

- How are women presented in the media? And men?
- What do they look like (in adverts, television programmes, magazines, etc.)?
- What roles are they given?
- Why is there so much nudity, or semi-nudity, in the media?
- Why is sex used to sell things that have nothing to do with sex?
- Why is sex an 'added ingredient' in so many television programmes?
- What is unrealistic about sex on television?
- Are sex stories in the newspapers reported in the same way as other stories?
- How often do the media show older people, especially women, as sexual?

SEXISM

Boys have got different sex things, and girls don't like playing football and boys do.
(10-YEAR-OLD BOY)

Children are very conscious of sexual difference. Even a baby senses the difference between the soft body, and probably the milky smell, of its mother and the harder, probably hairy, body of its father. Some children have their own very clear ideas about what the important sexual differences are.

Without a basic understanding of what is male and what is female, children can't begin to reach any understanding of human reproduction or human sexuality. So learning about difference is important. But it's easy for children to be confused about what the *real* differences are. It can be helpful, especially with children coming up to and around puberty, to try to identify the physical, inescapable differences between the sexes and to talk about what is, should or could be the same.

Children can develop very rigid ideas about male and female roles and it's worth challenging them so that they think about these things more flexibly. The box on the next page may help you. Try giving examples of famous people who don't fit the conventional roles, and talk about other families you know as well as the way things are in your own family. You could also try together to work out how these sexual stereotypes have come about, and how they affect you and your child. For example, how do the boys at school think about the girls, and vice versa? Are boys and girls treated differently? And so on.

145

WHAT'S DIFFERENT?

- Men and women have different sex organs that work in different ways.
- Women have breasts, men do not.
- Women usually have broader hips.
- Men are usually taller (though not always) and have stronger muscles.
- Women don't grow hair on their face.
- Men often go bald as they get older but women usually don't.
- Men's voices are usually deeper.

WHAT'S THE SAME?

Both men and women can:
- cook
- drive tractors
- look after babies
- play football
- cry
- be brave
- be ballet dancers
- knit and sew
- earn large amounts of money
- do the ironing
- be in the army
- change a wheel on the car
- carry handbags
- be nurses, or doctors

and much more.

It isn't only social roles that become stereotyped. Children can grow up to think in equally narrow and conventional ways about men's and women's sexual roles. They may think, for example, that the man is sexually dominant and the woman passive; that boys masturbate but girls do not; that men enjoy sex more than women do and that men are less emotional about it; that contraception is solely a woman's responsibility; or that a father is very little involved in the birth of his baby. They may not be told these things explicitly, but they learn them indirectly, from what *is* said to them and what is *not*. Certain things are often said to girls but not to boys and vice versa. They also learn these things from the media, where differences in sexual roles tend to be emphasized and where men and women are frequently shown in conventional sexual roles. For example, it is still women much more than men who are shown undressed, who are shown to be emotional, who receive rather than make sexual advances.

If children grow up with limited ideas about men's and women's roles (both social and sexual), their own choices in life may be equally limited. They are more likely to try to fit a mould than work out for themselves what is right for them and they can end up very frustrated and unhappy. This can apply to every part of their lives: the friends they choose, the jobs they want to do, their ambitions, attitudes and values . . . and the way they express their sexuality.

LEARNING ABOUT SEXUALITY

Your sexuality is *what you are*. It isn't just whether you are male or female, although it includes that. It isn't how you express yourself sexually, although it includes **147** that too. Your sexuality is the sexual part of your make-up, it's the sexual you.

Getting to know and understand your own sexuality takes time. It's a process that begins for everyone in childhood, and for some people it continues through adult life. It's a process that can be hindered by mistaken ideas about what men and women should be like sexually (see Sexism page 145), and by pressures from parents or from friends and other children to conform to what is seen as 'normality'.

It can be difficult for parents to admit that their children are sexual beings, just as it's hard to admit that they are growing up.

My mum doesn't really want me to have a boyfriend. I try to reassure her, but I can still feel sometimes that she doesn't want me to be growing up. It's like I asked her about contraception, and she automatically thinks I'm going to have sex with my boyfriend. She doesn't trust me, and that really hurts.
(15-YEAR-OLD GIRL.)

She thinks she's mature enough to understand things, but I don't think she is. She doesn't understand the pressure she may be under, you know, if a boy is coming on strong. She thinks she can handle that, but I honestly don't think she can, not at 14.

My parents worry about how I'm dressed and the way I present myself and the way I talk to people. . . . My mum is okay. My dad thinks I'm still his little girl and he wants me to stay at home, but my mum knows how it is to be a girl and wanting to grow up quickly.

(13-YEAR-OLD GIRL.)

Children *are* sexual, and they need their parents to acknowledge their sexuality so that they can begin to accept it themselves. They need to be able to understand that sexuality is not a matter of categories (heterosexual or homosexual, for example) but something very personal and a part of themselves. They need to understand that some people are *more* sexual than others (sex is very important for some people, less so for others, and for some not important at all); and that people may be more or less sexual at different stages in their lives.

Thinking about sexuality in these ways can help children develop a better, more sensitive understanding of homosexuality. This understanding is vital, for prejudiced and homophobic ideas are just as current in the playground as in society generally, and many children come to fear the possibility that they may be gay or lesbian. While probably few heterosexual parents find it easy to accept the idea that their child may be homosexual, most would not wish on their child the kind of unhappiness that results from living with the 'wrong' sexual identity.

I know a friend actually went to her mum and said, 'I fancy so and so, so I think I must be a lesbian.' And her mum said, 'You're too young to tell, you're only 12. Keep going, and if you find that you actually continue being interested in women, then we'll discuss that and that's fine.' And once her mum had said the word 'lesbian', she was able to go out and actually look it up and find out and talk about it and be comfortable. She is a lesbian, and she and her mum have got a really good relationship. They're fine with it.

> *I think parents should say there's nothing wrong with loving other women if you are a woman, and men if you're a man. There will be prejudice against you, and there will be problems, but if it makes you happy and it makes you a stronger person, if it makes you feel like who you really are rather than pretending all your life, then it's a better option. And they should say that they will support you. Then you will have that comfort and a way out if things get bad. Because if you feel like your parents have said, 'No, this is wrong, you're out,' then you feel discarded, you feel like there must be something wrong with you, you feel like you're bad, just because your parents can't handle the idea.*

Teenagers not only need to find out about and accept their own sexuality, they also need to learn how to use it appropriately. For parents this means letting go a bit and allowing some independence. You'll probably be able to do this more happily if you have some agreed limits, and if you feel reasonably confident that your child has the knowledge and understanding to cope with difficult social and sexual situations.

The kind of limits you could talk over and agree with your children are what time they have to come home at night, where they can and can't go, when they can bring friends back home and what's expected (say hello when you come in, do your own washing-up . . .), and so on. You might also agree that you should always know where they're going, that they should give you some idea (within an hour?) of when they'll be back, and that they should phone if their plans change. What's agreed will differ from one family to another, depending on you, your children, where

150

you live, what your children want to do, whether you have a car, etc.

If you can also give some support, it will make both you *and* your child feel more secure. It can help even the most confident teenager to know that they can always phone you if they need help and that you will come and pick them up, no questions asked. (It's worth making sure they have a phone card and money on them to be able to do this.)

And if you feel they may be in a situation where they will be sexually active, it helps if you can talk about ways they can protect themselves from pregnancy and STDs. It's always difficult to get the balance right between, on the one hand, not seeming to wish them into it, and on the other, making sure that, if they need to be, they are protected. But it's better to try to say something (preferably well before the time when they might choose to become sexually active), than to keep quiet for fear of saying the wrong thing. (For information about contraception and safer sex, see pages 112 to 117 and 137.

You also need to talk, and keep talking, to your children about ways of handling situations and relationships. It's important not to make the mistake of seeming to know it all. Keeping it as low key as you can (no matter if you're beside yourself with anxiety), and admitting to your own uncertainties not to mention your own past mistakes, is likely to work best.

Parents can't exactly teach you how to have a good relationship. But I think that they can tell you what their experiences were when they were your age and how they

151

> *coped with the pressure of having to have a boyfriend,*
> *and things like that.*
> (12-YEAR-OLD GIRL.)

> *I've told my daughters that it's okay to enjoy sex and that*
> *it's also okay to say, no, I'm not enjoying this, and this*
> *isn't right for me. And if somebody wants to touch you in*
> *a way that you're not happy with, then it's perfectly okay*
> *and it's right for you to say no.*

> *We've told them what is right and what is wrong, and*
> *they have to make their own choices. But if they do make*
> *any mistakes, we are always there to help and support*
> *them and pull them through.*

Helping children to handle their relationships successfully starts when they're very young. It's really only the
details that change as they get into their teens. At six
years old, your son comes home in tears because he'd
been teased at school. At eight years old, your daughter
is sad because no one will play with her. At 13 your son
is having difficulty keeping up with the gang. And at
16, your daughter is in tears because she's finished with
her boyfriend. In all these situations you're dealing
with the same kind of difficulties and trying to teach the
same kind of skills.

No one, of course, can get all these things right.
And no matter what you do, you can't make everything
'right' for your children. They, and you, have to accept
that they will sometimes make and maybe suffer from
mistakes. Staying friends despite this is what is most
important. See the box opposite for the skills that are
152 needed.

SKILLS FOR HANDLING RELATIONSHIPS

- Understanding and respecting other people.
- Respecting and standing up for yourself (knowing what's right for you, and how to say no).
- Recognizing and valuing the qualities you like in others.
- Recognizing the qualities you don't like.
- Knowing how to make, and be, friends.
- Knowing how to end a relationship kindly, and stay friends.
- Knowing how to react to praise.
- Knowing how to deal with criticism.
- Knowing how to deal with negative feelings (like sadness or disappointment).
- Knowing how to admit you've made a mistake.
- Knowing how to say you're sorry.
- Knowing how to ask for help.

PRESSURES AND CHOICES

A lot of my friends' breasts had already begun to develop, and mine hadn't. They were wearing bras and it was, you know, the thing to do, particularly when you were getting changed for PE. Well, my grandma, who was bedridden at the time, had a drawer full of underwear. And I just pinched one of her bras and washed it out secretly each week and hid it somewhere to dry and put it back on again. But I had to stuff it with socks, to look as if I had some. I remember going to a disco one night and

153

> *suddenly noticing that there was a sock on the floor which had definitely come out of my bra.*

Children are under enormous pressure to conform – to wear the right clothes, to have the right toys/sports equipment/digital watch, to have the right hair style, to like the right music . . . in other words, to look like everyone else looks and do what everyone else does. This kind of pressure can cause a lot of misery. All parents can tell a story of giving in and buying something they didn't like and couldn't afford, just so their child wouldn't feel 'out of it'.

The same sort of pressures to conform operate in the sexual world for children, from puberty or earlier.

> *The boys worry about being macho, they worry about how their bodies are going to develop, whether they'll have muscles, whether they'll have a long penis, whether they'll be able to make it, I suppose. More than anything else, how they're going to impress the girls.*
> (13-YEAR-OLD BOY.)

> *There's a lot of talk about who's going with who, and has she done it, or how far has she gone. They say, she's a slag, you know, for going with a boy, but they still go on about it.*
> (15-YEAR-OLD GIRL.)

> *There are pressures on boys not to be emotional or to show affection to other boys. Because if they do, they get classed as gays. In my brother's school, if boys wear their blazers buttoned up, they're gay.*
> (16-YEAR-OLD GIRL.)

154

The pressure to conform sexually is more serious. A girl who goes out with a boy, lets him touch her, maybe eventually has sex with him, just because she feels it's expected of her (and because she feels nobody, including the boy, will like her if she doesn't) can be made very unhappy by the experience. The same goes for a boy who feels he must have a girlfriend, when he would really be much happier in a group of boys.

Children need self-esteem and self-confidence to resist these sorts of pressures. It can be especially difficult for children who come from families with very strong moral or religious views or a culture which places them in a minority. Children with disabilities can also feel excluded from the social and sexual 'norms'. All children need to value themselves enough to be able to resist what other people tell them to do, if they need to.

> *I think my daughters have learned that you can look at two cultures and take good out of both and combine them to make your own culture. They've decided that their religion is important, their culture is important, but they also want to be able to make friends with people of different cultures and accept their values. I've tried to teach them that if they see their friends going off and having boyfriends, that's not wrong because that's acceptable within their culture. But you have to be sure of your own culture. If you're sure of your own culture, then you'll accept other people for what they are, and they'll accept you for what you are.*

If parents are aware of the pressures their children may be feeling, and realize how difficult it can be to resist, **155** they can help them to be aware of the choices that are really open to them. Try talking about it. For example, you could look at some of the feelings that are connected with conforming and not conforming. Start with something easy, such as why everyone wants to wear the same sort of trainers, what it means to look the same as everyone else, and how it would feel not to wear them. You can then move on to other pressures.

Children need to know that in some situations, no matter how pressured they feel, they can choose to say no. Many feel that this isn't a choice they can make, and it's true that there are many situations in which they *don't* have any choice – going to school, doing homework, helping at home, etc. Also, saying no can be hard, especially if you want to be liked. Try to talk about situations where saying no would be right, and about how they can say it, and about how people will really respect them for saying it. For example:

> *'What would you do if the friends you walk home from school with wanted to walk round the long way?'*
> *'I'd probably go with them.'*
> *'But that would make you late home. I'd be worried.'*
> *'I know. But how could I say no?'*
> *'You could just say it. It's usually best if you're very firm and clear about it, even if you don't feel like that. Just say, "I don't want to walk that way home."'*
> *'They'd try and persuade me.'*
> *'What about saying, "I can't. My mum would be worried." It helps if you give a reason.'*
> *'They might not think much of you.'*
> *'I think I can take that better than worrying about where you are.'*

THE RISK OF ABUSE

For me, it's the greatest anxiety, and the greatest horror. There are lots of things that I worry about for them, but there are no other anxieties where I feel so powerless to do anything. I just feel whatever I teach them, whatever I do, I can't protect them from people who intend to do them harm.

Children, including very young children, need to know and understand about personal risk, and they need to learn skills to protect themselves against abuse. Although you can't protect them completely, there is much that you *can* do.

Ignorance makes children very vulnerable, and clear, honest information about sex is protective. Children can't begin to know what kind of behaviour is acceptable and what is unacceptable unless they have at least basic information about the sexual parts of the body and what they are for. They need this information early. (See Bodies, pages 39 to 57).

At the same time, children need to be taught that *no one* has the right to touch their body, or do anything to them that they don't want or don't like or they feel is wrong. If anyone (even someone they know) does any of these things, then they should find someone they trust and explain what has happened. Be very clear about this. (You will probably need to explain that doctors and nurses *do* need to touch people and this is okay.)

Information about sex is protective, and so is information about abuse itself. Although some people feel that it frightens children unnecessarily to tell them

157

about abuse, children cannot recognize danger, or even inappropriate behaviour, if they don't know what they are looking for. At first, you'll need to talk very simply. For example: 'Most people care for children and would never harm them. But there are a few people who aren't like that. Some men, for example, want to show their penis to a child and may ask the child to touch his penis, or do other things. Some people want to watch children getting undressed, or want to touch their sexual parts. All of this is very wrong. Your body is yours, and no one should ever touch it, or ask you to touch them, like that.' If your child asks questions, try to answer very clearly and honestly, recognizing that what you say could be worrying and frightening. Explain, giving a lot of reassurance, that it's unlikely to happen, but that it's best to know what to do, just in case.

When your child is older, you can explain more. Older children will see and hear reports of abuse and other sexual offences in the media, and if you can talk about these it will help them understand and keep what they hear in proportion. Unless you explain, what they imagine may be even worse than the truth. Try to explain the terms – abuse, rape, assault, paedophile, etc. – in a factual way, emphasizing all the time that there are ways in which everyone can protect themselves against these offences.

You'll need to establish some simple rules and say very clearly what your child should do if he or she *is* approached or *is* abused. Young children should know beyond any doubt that they should not talk to strangers (of any age, men or women), or accept anything from strangers, or go anywhere with strangers, no matter what story is told or bribe is offered. And, since the majority of paedophiles are not strangers but are known to the child, you also need to warn your child about this and talk about what they should do if someone they know offers them a lift, or asks them to go for a walk or to visit their house. Warn, too, about the person who suggests sharing a 'secret', and explain there are times when it's okay for a child to tell. Try giving some examples of what might happen, and talk calmly and in a matter-of-fact way about what they could say and do. For example:

> *'If you were in the playground on your own, and someone came and suggested you walked down to the shops together for an ice-cream, what would you say?'*
> *'I'd say, no thanks.'*
> *'And what would you do then?'*
> *'I'd come back home and find you.'*
> *'Straightaway?'*
> *'Yes, straightaway.'*
> *'And if the person followed you, what would you do?'*
> *'I'd run away.'*
> *'Or you could go into the post office and explain to the lady in the post office what was happening and she could phone me.'*

Most schools do some work to help children understand about the danger of abuse and how to avoid it. This work usually begins in primary school. Try to follow up on what your child learns by talking about it at home.

TELLING IT AS IT IS

I think often as adults we're not honest with children. We try and tell children what we think they ought to know.

Sex isn't a subject that anyone can talk about completely objectively. Every parent has something that he or she finds especially difficult, or something he or she feels especially strongly about. We can't help but bring our own experience into what we say, no matter how impersonally we talk.

For children, that's probably a good thing. Children want and ask to know about emotions and experiences. They want to know if it's nice to make love, if it hurts to have a period, what it feels like to have a baby. And parents can usually answer these questions more successfully than teachers can. Describing how it feels to have a baby is fine at bathtime at home, or side-by-side in the car, or over the washing-up, but it's not appropriate for teachers to talk about their personal experiences to a class.

But for every parent, there's also a temptation to tell a bit less than the truth. When you're talking to someone who knows little, or certainly less than you do, and who'll believe you (at least for a day or two) if you say that babies are found under gooseberry bushes, it's tempting to avoid the more difficult and embarrassing subjects.

I don't think I'm in any position to talk about relationships since my own marriage has broken up, so I try to keep off the subject. I don't want her to think that that's what happens in every marriage.

160

I don't think homosexuality is an issue that need concern him. He's not likely to come across anyone who's homosexual, so I don't feel he needs to know about that, not at any rate until he's much older.

But children are already aware of many of the issues that we may try to avoid, and sometimes they have experience (for example of their parents' divorce) which means their need for information is urgent. No matter what your religious beliefs or moral values, no matter how hard or embarrassing you find it, children have a right to full, honest information. Half the truth can be as misleading as no information at all. It is wrong to suggest, for example, that sex only takes place within marriage, that HIV is only a problem for homosexuals, that all married couples live happily ever after, or that sexual intercourse always ends in orgasm.

Some parents feel that there is some information that children should not be given because it is 'too much' for them, or 'too difficult', at least while they are young. In fact, there is very little information that children can't accept, provided they are given it in a caring way, and in a way they can understand. You may need to say it more simply to very young children, but you can, usually, still say it. Ignorance, on the other hand, certainly *can* be unacceptable and can put children at risk. Tell the truth (and tell it gently) and the only risk is that you may stammer and blush a bit while you're doing it. No child ever worried about that.

USEFUL ORGANIZATIONS

Brook Advisory Centres
Central Office and Education and Publications Unit
153a East Street
London SE17 2SD
071–708 1234/1390
24-hour helpline: 071-617 8000
*Advice, help and information for young people on personal
relationships, contraception, pregnancy, abortion and sexually
transmitted diseases. Centres around the country. Free
publications list.*

Childline
Freepost 1111
London N1 0BR
0800 1111
*Children can phone free of charge, 24 hours a day, or write (no
stamp needed), if they are in trouble and want to talk. It's
completely confidential.*

Family Planning Association
27–35 Mortimer Street
London W1N 7RJ
071–636 7866
*Phone this number to find the address of the family planning clinic
nearest to you. The FPA also runs a free information service and
produces free leaflets and booklets. You can send for a free list of
health education materials by sending an A5 SAE to the Healthwise
Bookshop at the same address.*

Health Education Authority
Hamilton House
Mabledon Place
London WC1H 9TX
071–383 3833
*The HEA's Information Service can tell you the address of your
nearest Health Promotion Unit where you can get free publications
on a range of health topics. Or look in your local phone book under*

the name of your district health authority. Contact the HEA for a
free publications list.

National AIDS Helpline

0800 567123

Free, confidential, 24-hour advice and information service about
HIV and AIDS. If you are deaf or hard of hearing, you can phone
Minicom on 0800 521361 between 10am and 10pm. The National
AIDS Helpline is staffed by people who speak:

– Bengali, Gujarati, Hindi, Punjabi, Urdu and English on
Wednesdays, 6pm to 10pm. Phone 0800 282445

– Chinese (Cantonese) and English on Tuesdays, 6pm to 10pm.
Phone 0800 282466

– Arabic and English on Wednesdays, 6pm to 10pm. Phone 0800
282447.

– Afro Carribbean and English on Fridays, 6pm to 10pm. Phone
0800 282445

Leaflets are also available in these languages and can be ordered by
phoning 0800 555777.

– Information is available in Brail via: RNIB, 224 Great Portland
Street, London.

– Audio cassettes are available if you send a C60 blank tape to:
Playback, 276 St Vincent Street, Glasgow.

National Childbirth Trust

Alexandra House
Oldham Terrace
Acton
London W3 6NH
081–992 8637
Information and advice on pregnancy and childbirth.

Parent Network

44–46 Caversham Road
London NW5 2DS
071–485 8535
Support for parents. Helps parents to develop better relationships
with their children. Phone to find out if there is a local support
group near you.

163

Relate Marriage Guidance
Herbert Gray College
Little Church Street
Rugby CV21 3AP
0788 573241
Counselling for people with relationship, marriage or sexual problems.
Phone for information about the branch of Relate nearest to you.

Sex Education Forum
National Children's Bureau
8 Wakeley Street
London EC1V 7QE
071–278 9441
An umbrella group representing organizations involved in giving
support and information to people who provide sex education to
young people.

SPOD (Association to Aid the Sexual and Personal Relationships of People with a Disability)
286 Camden Road
London N7 0BJ
071–607 8851
Information and advice on disability and sexuality.

The Terrence Higgins Trust
52–54 Grays Inn Road
- London WC1X 8JU
071–831 0330 (Administration and Advice Centre)
071–242 1010 (Helpline 3pm to 10pm daily)
Practical support, help, counselling and advice for anyone with, or
concerned about, AIDS and HIV infection.

Youth Access
Magazine Business Centre
11 Newarke Street
Leicester LE1 5SS
0533 558763
Referral agency. Phone this number to find out if there is a young
people's counselling service near you.

BOOK LIST

In addition to the books and booklets listed here, many of the organizations on pages 162 to 164 produce helpful publications. Phone or write to them for details.

This list is divided into four groups: publications for younger children, those for children aged ten plus, those for teenagers, and those for parents and teachers. But it is difficult to generalize about what book is suitable for children at what age. What one ten year old might be ready for and understand, another might not. Parents too have very different views about what their children should see and read. So look first at any book or booklet you are giving to your child, to decide whether you think it will be helpful.

Some of the publications that are available by post from organizations are free, others are not! Phone or write for details.

For younger children

The body book by Claire Rayner. DEUTSCH, 1978; PICCOLO, 1979.

Happy children, sad children From: NSPCC, Publicity Unit, Ref 910418, 67 Saffron Hill, London EC1N 8RS.
About abuse, for parents and children to read together.

How you began: a story in pictures by L Nilsson. KESTREL BOOKS, 1975.

The joy of birth by Camilla Jessel. METHUEN, 1982.
Black and white photographs to explain the miracle of birth. For parents and children to look at together.

See how you grow by P Pearse. MACDONALD, 1988.
A book with lift-up flaps.

We can say no by David Pithers and Sarah Greene. BEAVER BOOKS, in association with the National Children's Home, 1986.
Protecting yourself from dangerous people.

What's wrong with bottoms? by J Hessell. HUTCHINSON, 1987.
Story to help parents talk to young children about sexual abuse.

For children aged ten plus

Facts of life by S Meredith. USBORNE, 1985.

Have you started yet? by R Thomas. PICCOLO, 1980.

How your body changes: Information for boys and girls
From: the Family Planning Association, address on page 162.

It's OK to be you! Feeling good about growing up by Claire
Patterson and Lindsay Quilter. PICCOLO, 1991.

What can I do about AIDS? From: the Terrence Higgins Trust,
address on page 164, or from Barnardos, Tanners Lane,
Barkingside, Ilford, Essex IG6 IQG.
To help children understand about AIDS.

For teenagers

Christianity and homosexuality. A resource for students The
Lesbian and Gay Christian Movement, 1992. From: LGCM,
Oxford House, Derbyshire Street, London E2 6HG.

The diary of a teenage health freak by Aidan Macfarlane and
Ann McPherson. OXFORD UNIVERSITY PRESS, 1987.
Diary of a 14-year-old boy.

I'm a health freak too! by Aidan Macfarlane and Ann
McPherson. OXFORD UNIVERSITY PRESS, 1989.
*By the same authors as **The diary of a teenage health freak** (see
above), this is the diary of the original health freak's 16 year old
sister.*

It's more than sex. A survival guide to the teenage years by
Suzie Hayman. WILDWOOD HOUSE, 1986.

No is not enough by Caren Adams, Jennifer Fay and Jan
Loreen-Martin. Lions Choices, COLLINS, 1984.
Advice on how teenagers can be protected against sexual assault.

Safe, strong and streetwise: A teenage survival guide by Helen
Benedict. Lightning Series, HODDER & STOUGHTON, 1987.

Say yes, say no, say maybe from Brook Advisory Centres,
address on page 162.
*A booklet on safer sex, researched and written especially for older
teenagers. Takes a realistic view of teenagers' attitudes and needs.*

Sex education dictionary by Gill Mullinar. LDA, WISBECH,
CAMBRIDGESHIRE, 1992.
*For teenagers. Definitions of words to do with sex, including
common slang words.*

Sexuality: Information for young adults From: the Family
Planning Association, address on page 162.

Speaking out about abuse. What every young person should know From: NSPCC, Publicity Unit, Ref 910419, 67 Saffron Hill, London EC1N 8RS.

For parents and teachers

AIDS in the family. Information for parents and carers of children From: the Terrence Higgins Trust, address on page 164, or from Barnados, Tanners Row, Barkingside, Ilford, Essex IG6 1QG.

Answering your child's questions. Information for parents From: the Family Planning Association, address on page 162.

Curriculum guidance no 5: Health education NATIONAL CURRICULUM COUNCIL, 1990. From: the National Curriculum Council, 15–17 New Street, York, YO1 2RA.
Guidance for schools on the content of school sex education. Also useful for interested parents.

A framework for school sex education From: the Sex Education Forum, address on page 164.
A leaflet outlining the knowledge, social skills, attitudes and values appropriate in school sex education.

Growing pains: What to do when your children turn into teenagers by David Bennett. THORSONS, 1987.

Living with a teenager by Suzie Hayman. PIATKUS, 1988.

Our bodies, ourselves edited by Angela Phillips and Jill Rakusen. PENGUIN, 1989.

Sex education for young people with a physical disability. A guide for teachers and parents by Mary Davies. From: SPOD (Association to Aid the Sexual and Personal Relationships of People with a Disability), address on page 164.

Show me yours. What children think about sex by Ronald and Juliette Goldman. PENGUIN, 1988.

Teenagers. A family survival guide by Laurie Graham. CHATTO & WINDUS, 1992.

Teenagers and sexuality by John Coleman. An audio cassette and booklet. From: the Trust for the Study of Adolescence, 23 New Road, Brighton, East Sussex BN1 1WZ
On the tape, parents and teenagers talk about their experiences.

167

INDEX

Page numbers in *italic* refer to the illustrations